Guide for the Care of Infants in Groups

SALLY PROVENCE, M.D.

Director
Child Development Unit
Yale University Child Study Center

I-32
$2.50
1967

Child Welfare League of America, Inc.
44 East 23rd Street, New York, N.Y. 10010

Foreword

In 1962 I was asked to write a review of a book by Dr. Sally Provence and Dr. Rose C. Lipton: *Infants in Institutions—A Comparison of Their Development with Family-Reared Infants During the First Year of Life*. In their introduction, the authors state their belief that "the family . . . is the setting in which babies can best be provided with the care and influences that support and foster good development. It becomes increasingly hard to provide such care as we get farther away from this model. The infant's needs are multiple and complex, and it is difficult or perhaps impossible to meet them adequately under conditions of group care." Their report indicated why this is so, and the study method highlighted what kinds of care and stimulation are most obviously lacking in most group living situations for infants.

Since we know that many infants *are* in institutions, and a good number *will* regrettably spend the first years of their lives in such settings, it seemed that there would be value in a book that outlined what must be provided to support the healthy development of infants in group living situations, to minimize the hazards of such care, and to avoid doing irreparable damage to these infants.

In its November 1962 meeting, the League's Board of Directors considered the League policy not to accept for membership or to reaccredit agencies providing group care for children under the age of 6. While this policy had encouraged better planning for the care of infants and children, the League recognized that there was more that might be done to help agencies provide better care for those infants that do remain in institutions for whatever reason. Also, some agencies noted that they use institution care for infants up to 3 months only, while placement or adoption plans are worked out.

The Board modified the League membership policy at this time and approved that "the League may admit to membership, or retain in membership, an agency which provides group care for infants under three months of age when it is determined that the quality of care meets standards."

The Board also authorized the staff to offer consultation to institutions providing care for children up to the age of 6 and to develop guides for the care of infants in institutions. Subsequently, Dr. Provence accepted our invitation to prepare material that would serve such a purpose. Mrs. Zitha R. Turitz, Director of Standards Development, carried staff responsibility for working with Dr. Provence in planning for the writing of this guide.

We are most fortunate in having been able to bring so able and experienced a pediatrician and so lucid a writer as Dr. Provence to this task. She has a special empathy for infants that enables her to feel "what is going on with them" and to communicate it to the reader.

We also wish to acknowledge the financial support for this undertaking given by the Field Foundation.

We commend this guide to those who care for infants directly, to those who plan and administer the programs and facilities for such care, and to the boards and other community leaders who must see to it that the requirements for good care of infants are provided.

JOSEPH H. REID
Executive Director
Child Welfare League of America

Contents

Why This Guide Was Written

The publication of this guide may be taken by some to mean that the Child Welfare League of America and the author approve of group care for children in the first and second years. Nothing could be further from the truth. As indicated in 1962 in a statement of policy of the Child Welfare League of America, "Research and clinical experience have given evidence that group care for pre-school children may result in emotional and intellectual damage." During the past 15 years, in particular, there has been a strong movement to provide family care for infants without families. Efforts are being made with success in some communities to find more effective ways of helping parents care for their own children through such aids as increased financial support, assistance with household duties and child care, nursery schools, and day care arrangements. The development of a greater number of suitable foster homes through more vigorous recruiting and through providing these same aids to foster parents is another important and often effective measure. In this guide, however, we start from the undeniable fact that, under the present conditions in our society, group care of infants is a reality, however regrettable. According to the Children's Bureau, there were

77,300 children residing in 1483 institutions for dependent and neglected children on March 3, 1964, a reduction of about 5 percent from the Bureau's estimate for 1960.[1] Although these institutions tend to be small (70 percent reported a population of fewer than 50 children), 11 percent of the children were in institutions that accommodated as many as 300.[2]

We do not deal in this guide with the crucially important questions that are being studied and debated in the literature concerning the long-term effects of deprivation or the effects of multiple mothering or changes in the child's living situation. There are many other relevant questions ranging from an interest in variations in individual development to questions of concern to the society: Will there be significant differences in the personality structure of children reared in groups by persons not their own parents compared with children reared in families? Will children reared largely in group settings be able as adults to form families and care for their own children? How does a long period of group care, with the many parent figures inevitably involved, influence such aspects of personality as the development of internalized controls over behavior or the capacity to love? What are its effects on intellectual development and on creativity? How will our society be influenced if large numbers of its members are reared from infancy in group care settings? If a family in which an infant is living fails to provide him with good care and is frankly neglectful or abusive, at what point is such a living situation worse for his long-term development than a well-planned group care setting? How many changes can a child

1. Seth Low, *America's Children and Youth in Institutions: A Demographic Analysis* (Washington, D.C.: U.S. Government Printing Office, 1965), p. 17.
2. *Ibid.*, p. 15.

tolerate—for example, a series of foster homes or substitute parents—and still have a better chance for development than if he grows up in group care?

These are but a few of the important questions that can and should be asked about group care, and they will not soon be answered. No discussion of them will be attempted here.

This guide is based on a simple thesis: Infants should be well cared for. We know enough about their development and their needs to know what constitutes good care. What happens after age 2 is important, of course, but our purpose is to emphasize that, regardless of what comes later, there are experiences and developmental tasks that ought to be part of infancy. For these the infant is dependent upon people entrusted with his care.

SALLY PROVENCE

CHAPTER ONE

Introduction

Most books on child care are for parents; their emphasis is on how care should be given. They usually take for granted the love that most parents have for their own children, and assume that a mother's intuition will guarantee that the necessary stimulation—physical, social, intellectual, and emotional—is provided.

This guide is for child care workers and others responsible for providing care for infants without families. An effort has been made to include some of the "why's" of child care, because knowing more about how babies grow and develop and why they need what they need makes it more likely that the most important ingredients of good child care will be supplied. The text, therefore, is partly about how babies develop (Chapters 1 through 6) and partly about how to care for them (Chapters 7 through 15).

Institution Care Ought To Be Done Well

In preparing this guide, we have taken the noncontroversial position that wherever institution care exists, it ought to be done well. Therefore we attempt to communicate some concepts of development in the first two years of life and to recommend specific child care practices in group care of infants that will support the child's development rather than interfere with it.

There is little disagreement about the adverse effects of deprivation upon infant development, and no knowledgeable person would now recommend that infants be cared for in groups where only their needs for food, clothing, and shelter are met. It appears that group care can be planned that will avoid the more serious effects of deprivation. But the question of precisely how a group care setting can provide care, stimulation, and learning experiences to influence development in a favorable way is another matter.

One of the unanswered questions in regard to group care concerns the matter of the development of a personal and group identity of young children reared entirely in a group by several caretakers. Nor do we know how this method of child rearing will influence these children's capacity to become parents and form stable families of their own. These questions can be answered only by meticulous, long-term studies of children reared in good group care settings. We can be comforted by our knowledge that children are resilient and adaptable, but we must not use their flexibility to justify inadequate child care practices.

Facts About Infant Development

In order to introduce the reader, a few of the facts on which this material is based are listed below.

Most Infants Are Normal

1. Most infants (at least 90 percent) are born with the capacity to develop normally; it is important that we make every effort to help them do so by caring for them in such a way that their development is supported rather than interfered with.

Infants Need Tangibles and Intangibles

2. When we refer to the infant's needs, we mean certain kinds of supplies and relief that he requires. Some of his needs have to do with the care, protection, and comfort of his body. Others have to do with the growth of his

mind and with his development as a social being who must gradually learn to make his way in a complicated world.

Quantity and Quality of Care

3. The amount and kind of care that an infant receives is crucial to the way he will develop. This amount is not the same for every baby, but without enough care, development will not progress normally. The kind of care the baby receives should be personalized care. This refers to two things: (1) He needs to be cared for by a person who can love and be interested in him, and (2) he needs someone to answer his specific needs. A baby who is fed when he is hungry, warmed when he is cold, comforted when he is in distress has a much better chance of developing and learning than one who is cared for according to someone else's schedule that has little to do with his needs.

The Importance of the Mothering Person

We believe that to have the best chance to develop, infants need to be cared for mainly by one person. Although an infant can accept substitutes, there should be one main caretaker with whom he can form a special attachment. He is dependent on this mothering person for protection and the care of his body; but his early social and emotional needs, too, are met through her care, and most of the influences of the environment come to him through her.

The Importance of Ordinary Procedures

The ordinary procedures of care provide basic learning experiences for the infant; without them, his development would suffer. At the feeding, the bath, the changing of clothes, and many other daily experiences, he is stimulated, comforted, and communicated with; through these situations, he learns. For example, he learns that somebody will come when he cries, because somebody does come when he cries. He learns to distinguish between one person and another by comparing the difference between the appearance and behavior of the person who is repeatedly with him and that of another.

The Contribution of the Environment

4. The development of every child is a dynamic unfolding process. He starts life with certain inborn bodily and mental potentials that mature according to a biological timetable. However, these emerging abilities must be stimulated, reinforced, and organized into action units in order that adaptation and learning may proceed. This is where the child's environment comes in. The proposition can be stated thus: The abilities to walk, to think, to speak, to love come about as the result of a growth process combined with experience. Both the child's biological endowment and his environment are essential elements in his development.

Infants Are Durable and Resilient

5. There is no doubt that the infant's development suffers in many ways if he is in a depriving, confusing, or severely disturbed environment. But we are also impressed that the human being has considerable capacity for recovery; there is a drive toward health and harmony in development that is a part of human nature. This fact is encouraging. We must remember, however, that there is such a thing as too much stress, too much deprivation; and the infant's ability to adapt to stress or to recover from deprivation or hurt can be overtaxed. Most of the infants with whom we are concerned are in danger of being overtaxed. Therefore, it is important that the care they are given be wisely planned to serve their best interests.

CHAPTER TWO

Relationships to People and Emotional Growth

The Infant Reacts to People

How does a baby react to other people? How do his social and emotional relationships grow? In what way does a child learn to love others? Why are the people who care for him so important? Why do we believe that the amount and kind of care he receives in his earliest years affect his intellectual and emotional development? How can we foster his ability to establish close relationships with people?

We readily accept that a newborn baby is dependent on adults to take care of his bodily needs. But he has other needs too, and we know that he will not develop normally, emotionally and intellectually, without care and attention from adults. His reactions to people indicate his state of well-being and his progress. We will trace some of these reactions in considering the questions above.

The Early Communications

From his first day, the infant interacts with people. In the beginning, most of his social contacts occur as his bodily needs are being met. Many experiences in which something happens between the baby and another person are a part of his daily life. At first, he can express his states of comfort or discomfort only in the way he behaves. We say that the person who cares for him "reads" the behavior

Behavior Changes

changes and decides what to do for him. Her skill in this

will depend upon her own personality (she may be a "natural" in the care of babies) and also, of course, upon how much experience she has had.

Facial Expressions

At first, the baby's facial expression is vague, and his eyes focus on the adult for only a few seconds at a time; if restless or crying he may become quiet when spoken to or lifted; he may frown or smile. But we do not believe that he has clearly formed thoughts at this time.

The Social Smile

More specific reactions develop gradually. By the second and third month, the baby definitely smiles at another person. He adjusts his body when picked up and held. He follows a person with his eyes across the room. He vocalizes when spoken to. By the third and fourth months, he responds with much smiling, musical cooing, and increased body activity when someone smiles at, speaks to, or touches him. He is likely to be responsive to everyone at this age, but he responds most strongly to

Recognition of the "Mother"

the person who cares for him, and we believe that this is the first clear sign of his recognizing her. By about the fourth month, he is capable of a strong, definite show of displeasure when the contact with the person who cares for him is broken, and he may cry in protest when this adult moves out of sight or sound.

Gradually there are indications that the infant can distinguish between the face of a person and other objects that he looks at. From about the fourth month, there are signs that he anticipates situations in which the adult does

Recognition of the Bottle

something with and for him, such as his feeding. He recognizes the bottle and shows some eagerness about what is going to happen when the feeding is being prepared. It is of interest also that he now can wait a few moments for the bottle. We believe that this is one of the first signs that an infant is capable of remembering: He sees the bottle and becomes excited because he recognizes it as some-

First Signs of Memory and Anticipation

that he is going to get it. Of course, at this age he cannot thing he wants, but now he can wait a few moments without crying because he remembers from past experience wait long and should not be asked to. His memory is short, but the first signs of waiting with anticipation are there.

Sense of Confidence or Trust

We believe that this behavior also means that the baby is developing a sense of confidence that he is going to be cared for; this basic trust is important because it is the foundation on which future relationships will be built. It is strengthened by such experiences as being fed when he is hungry, being warmed when he is cold, and being comforted when he is uncomfortable. The following is a pattern of what probably happens: The baby feels discomfort; he cries and his crying brings the adult who makes him comfortable. At first, the infant probably recognizes the total experience that is responsible for the comfort, but later (some time around 4 months), he starts to show signs of recognizing the particular person who provides

The Beginnings of Love

the comfort and pleasure. We can say that he now enters into the first love relationship with another person. This ability to love will grow slowly and steadily, becoming more and more complicated, but it is well to remember that the care in the early months is vitally important to its development: The infant learns to love and to trust because of the way he is cared for (see also Chapter 7 on the role of the adult).

Reaction to the Strange

At about 4 to 6 months, we see a reaction in most infants that has been called an anxiety reaction to the strange. The infant, who previously has accepted everyone quite amiably, shows signs of anxiety when an unfamiliar person appears. He may cry with obvious distress. In the everyday situation, this is likely to happen for the first time when someone approaches whose hair color or tone of voice differs markedly from that of the adults to whom he is accustomed, or when someone familiar is wearing glasses or a hat or in some other way appears different than usual. The infant may also cry when he is taken to an unfamiliar place. We mention this phase of development because it indicates another aspect of growth in the infant's ability to discriminate and to express psychological, as contrasted with physical, distress. This awareness, which sharpens the distinction between the "safe" and the "unsafe" people, probably helps strengthen existing attachments.

He Signals . . . In the second half of the first year, the baby's contacts with people rapidly become more varied and complicated. He uses his voice to produce many different sounds that denote pleasure, excitement, anger, eagerness, delight, and protest. He gives signals with his voice; for example, when he wants attention, he can do something other than cry. An infant who does not begin to communicate in this way in the second half of the first year should make us wonder what is wrong with him. It may be that he does not hear, for hearing is important to vocalization; it may be that he has an underdeveloped brain; but most often—especially in a group care situation—it means that there has not been enough contact and communication with the persons who care for him. The infant who does not have individualized care from a person who speaks to and handles him, who takes care of his bodily needs, who communicates with him in many ways, often becomes subdued and apathetic and does not express the variety of feelings and the awareness described above. The infant who does have such care not only gives signals, but also behaves as if he *. . . Expecting a* expects a response to these signals. For example, an infant *Response* of 9 or 10 months whose mother is out of sight in another room will call her with a sharp "aaahn" sound and look expectantly toward the door for her to appear. This shows further development of his ability to remember and to develop mental images of the people in his world; they now begin to exist in his mind, even when they are out of sight.

The Infant's Feelings Become More Complicated

He has many facial expressions that indicate how he feels and make it easier for others to understand him. His emotions are becoming more complicated. Not only the old pleasure-displeasure feelings are found, but also other feelings: He may show anxiety, confusion, curiosity, or puzzlement; he appears at times playful, tender, angry, or gleeful. Furthermore, he may shift rapidly from one mood to another.

Initiative and Avoidance

If he is developing in a healthy way during the second half of the first year, he is able to be more active both in making contact with a person and in avoiding or rejecting such contact. When doing this, he uses the various skills that he has developed: he may make a contact with another person by smiling, by using his voice, or by looking; he may hold out a toy, sometimes giving it to the other person, sometimes pulling it back in a playful way; if he is held in the arms of the adult, he may gently pat her face or finger her nose or mouth or not so gently pull her hair or push her away. In other words, he expresses his wish for contact, as well as his ability to turn away or to refuse it.

Playfulness and Imitation

We see at this time, too, a rapid development of interest and ability to imitate that continues and becomes more complicated as time passes. We are all familiar with the games played with babies, such as peek-a-boo, pat-a-cake, bye-bye, and so-big. The response to peek-a-boo is usually seen at about 8 months; pat-a-cake, bye-bye, and so-big about a month later. At first, the baby imitates an adult; later he starts these games on his own and expects the adult to respond. Again, the baby who is not playful should arouse concern. An infant who has not had enough nurturing care is often apathetic; he does not enter vigorously into or initiate playful interchanges with others.

Asserting and Defending Himself

Another sign of healthy growth is that a child can use the various skills he has developed to defend or assert himself. He can pull hard on a toy, insisting on his right to have it. He can push away the hand of the adult, try to wriggle out of her arms, or go away from something he does not like. He can shake his head "no"; he can turn, roll, or crawl away from something he fears or dislikes. This reaction can be considered the beginning of two responses that he will use all of his life when he encounters problems in the outside world or inside himself: Sometimes he will stand and fight; sometimes he will go away. Both reactions are necessary and useful, and their beginnings are seen in the first year.

There are other things, too, of importance at this time. As mentioned earlier, the baby of 6 to 12 months shows signs of attachment to the mothering person by his recognition of her, his ability to remember her for short periods of time, his pleasure in seeing her, and his trust that she will respond to his needs. He also shows his attachment by reactions of anxiety at separation. We are all familiar with the infant of 9 to 12 months who clings to his mother, and with his distressed reactions at being separated from her. We believe that this kind of reaction, which we call "separation anxiety," is a feeling that all well-cared-for babies have. In some, it is easy to see; in others, it is less dramatic. It means that a new step has been taken: The

Separation Anxiety

infant has begun to realize that this person who has become so important to him can also be lost. To some extent, this feeling continues to exist as a fear all his life, but it is a developmental event of special significance in the last part of the first year and in the beginning of the second. Children brought up in group situations usually have either no visible reaction to separation from their caretakers or a reaction that is much less intense than that of children reared in families where a close tie to the mother has developed. This is apparently because there are usually many caretakers who come and go, so that a baby has no opportunity to establish a close tie.

Establishing
Close Ties
One of the goals in group care should be to provide each baby with a person with whom he can form a close relationship, because it is of enormous importance to his later development that he take these first steps in learning to love. One might ask whether it is cruel to make such a recommendation when it is probable that the caretakers will leave or the infant will be moved. But we are convinced that the infant has a better chance to develop adequately in every way if he forms such a close attachment, even if he loses his "mother" and has a separation or mourning reaction. He may temporarily mistrust the new mother or may be upset in other ways. Even so, he retains a greater capacity for further development than does the baby who never experiences the pleasure of a close relationship that carries with it the sharp experience at separation.

One works, then, to help the baby in group care to form a close attachment, and also to help him cope with the feelings that occur when there is a loss. When separation experiences—permanent or of more than a few days' duration—are anticipated, it is helpful to the child that the substitute or new caretaker know something about him and that she be introduced to him by his main "mother." This permits him to shift at least some of his trust and affection to the new person.

He Accepts Substitutes for the Mothering Person

There is another facet of normal development of infants that is reassuring because it emphasizes that the infant grows in ability and adaptation. Along with the attachment to the mother and the fear of loss, the baby can also develop meaningful attachments to other people and can accept and trust them. In a family, this attachment is often formed with the father, but it may be made with another adult or, at times, with an older child. Thus the infant can accept another person who cares for him without having his main attachment disturbed, and this stimulates another kind of growth experience: the world in which he is comfortable and secure has expanded.

Introducing Men

Since a group care setting for infants is usually staffed almost entirely by women, it is important to find ways of introducing men into the child's life.

Too Many Caretakers

But the matter of substitutes for the primary person should not be overdone. Unfortunately, the most frequent pattern is one of too many caretakers and too much change; this is dangerous because it overtaxes the infant's ability to adapt and results in serious disturbances in his development, such as disturbances in feeding, sleep, or physical health; apathy or deviations in social and emotional reactions; and delayed learning in respect to speech and the capacity to play. Substitute caretakers should be few in number and should not disrupt the infant's primary attachment. One must not mistake the blandness and indiscriminate friendliness that characterizes many infants who have had multiple caretakers for healthy emotional development.

Modes of Self-Comfort

Another kind of substitute for the mother is also accepted gradually. This is usually an object to which the infant becomes attached. He may be comforted for a short time in his mother's absence by his bottle or by a favorite teddy bear or by his blanket. We believe that it is an important development that he has some partial protection against his fear of loss: he can accept a familiar person as a substitute; he can comfort himself with thumb or bottle; he can cuddle his favorite toy. Thus, although the infant is still very dependent and needful of care, we see signs of development of resources for coping with stress.

The Second Year As we would expect, in the second year, the child's relationships to others become still more complicated. Maturation and experience bring about changes in his rhythms, abilities, feelings, and interests. His ability to walk alone and to do many things for himself goes hand-in-hand with progress in his mental development that has made him more aware of his own separate body and person. He has developed a strong enough attachment to the adults in his life to want to please them and win their approval. At the same time, he is stronger and more determined in his refusals. In the twinkling of an eye, he may shift from appearing in proud and masterful control—as he feeds himself, strides about, or asserts his wants—to being a helpless, forlorn baby when fatigue, disappointment, or anxiety overtake him.

He Wants To Please The toddler's attachment to people and his wish to please them becomes a powerful tool in the adult's efforts to help him learn to conform to some of society's expectations. Training in self-feeding, in controlling some of his behavior toward other people, and in controlling his bowel function are some of the areas commonly focused on in the second year. We assign the toddler the task of at least beginning, with our help, to exert some control in these areas, and we expect him to learn to respect certain prohibitions. The "no" may be the most frequently used (often overworked) word in the adult's vocabulary at this time, but it is essential to the infant's learning.

Negativism

One of the characteristics of the child in his second year has been described as negativism. Having encountered the word "no" and learned some of its uses, the toddler begins to say "no" to practically everything. This often includes what he does want, as well as what he does not want. He may even say "no" as he moves to comply with the adult's request, "Do you want to go outside?" "No," he answers, as he goes toward the door. "Do you want some more milk?" "No," he says, as he reaches for the glass. Often, however, he means what he says emphatically and protests vigorously any attempt by the adult to interfere. He may protest the demands placed upon him by reacting against toilet training, by withholding, or by soiling. He may object by acting aggressively toward others or by running away. His protest is a normal developmental step, which expresses his ability to assert himself. As he becomes more a person with his own wishes and ideas, he wants to do more for himself. As he becomes more assertive, he also develops a greater capacity for fun and pleasure. He has an increasingly complicated set of feelings; his repertoire of emotions grows in size and strength just as his body does. Exuberance, joy, anger, anxiety, bewilderment, disappointment, curiosity, disgust, and other emotions are there.

Independence

Strong Emotions

Regression

The contrast between behavior that denotes the struggle toward independence and behavior that is more infantile is dramatic in the second year. The return to more babyish forms of behavior we refer to as regression. Regression is an everyday occurrence when the child becomes tired, ill, hungry, or upset for any reason. Rest, comfort, and loving care permit the child again to express the forward thrust of his development.

At the same time that he is becoming more independent and more aware of himself as a separate person, the child is strengthening his bonds to the people in his life. He has become aware of their importance to him in providing *Strong* comfort, protection, and pleasure. A separation from the *Attachments* parent figures at such a time often upsets the child. This may show itself in disturbances in feeding, sleep, toilet habits, or play; he may appear apathetic, depressed, or bereaved. The extent of the reaction will depend on many things: the length of the separation, the conditions that led up to it, who the substitute caretakers are, and even the child's state of health at the time. It is easy for adults to discount the impact on the child of such separations. It is true that the child is still so dependent on the adults for his most basic bodily care that he will accept this from almost anyone. We should remember, however, that specific adults have special meaning for him and are important in his development: They cannot be exchanged willy-nilly for others, if we expect healthy mental development.

We have only to look at a child of 1 to 2 years old to be impressed both with his growing self-reliance and his continued need for the adult. An 18-month-old walks across the room and plays for a while with his toys, but soon he looks up to find the familiar adult with his eyes, or comes back and sits near her or leans against her for a few moments. He then resumes his play. This common event is *Recharging* like a "recharging of the battery" for the child. A few *the Battery* minutes of closeness to the adult permits him to return to his play contented. A little later, when he is almost 2, he may leave his play and come in from out-of-doors to find the adult. Of course, this may be when he is hurt or upset and needs comfort, but it also occurs when there is no obvious trouble and it reflects his need to reestablish contact, to reassure himself that the adult is still around and cares

*Approval and
Disapproval*

for him. It is another sign of intellectual and emotional growth: The infant now has developed enough awareness of the importance of the adult to become concerned not only about whether she is there for him, but also whether she approves or disapproves of his behavior. This gradually developing state of affairs is an important part of the process of learning to live with others.

*Increase in
Aggression*

Another healthy step in development seen in the second year is the increase of aggressive behavior in the child. Aggressive feelings are a normal part of the human being. All human relationships are permanently influenced by the fact that the earliest love relationships are formed when the ones whom the child loves are those who both indulge and limit him. Thus the child has both positive and negative feelings about them. In the 1- to 2-year-old, the aggressive feelings often are expressed in angry crying, throwing, hitting, and biting. Aggression is not "bad"; it is necessary to survival and to learning. What we strive for is the control of aggressive behavior and the channeling of aggressive energy into constructive activity. Learning to control and transform the aggressive feelings takes a long time, and this, as well as other controls over behavior, develops most favorably when the education and guidance, which are esential, take place in an atmosphere in which the adult communicates interest and tenderness as well as guidance.

*Imitation and Early
Identification*

In many of his actions in the second year, the child imitates what he sees adults doing. We note his interest in doing household tasks: He wants to dust, sweep, or wash the dishes; in his play with a doll, he reenacts what is done to and for him. He also begins to copy the adults' tone of voice and, at times, their attitudes: disgust at messiness, shame at misbehavior, pleasure at the arrival of a friend, sympathy for a person in distress. These attitudes, of course, are still in their nascent state and quickly vanish when the child's own inclinations lead him in another direction. But this illustrates one of the processes through which the child incorporates the models provided by the adults, and how these models gradually become a part of his own personality and standards. We call this process identification with the adult. The child participates in their reactions and emulates their methods of solving problems and coping with emergencies. In assuming their attitudes and methods, he strengthens his ability to control his own impulses. This is a process that extends far beyond the first two years. It is mentioned here only to illustrate still another way in which the adult is of importance to the child.

Summary By the time he is 2 years old, the infant has come a long way in his relationships to people. He knows the names of parents and other children; he says words that indicate his awareness of other people and what they are doing; and he has learned to understand the "no" of the adult, although he does not always respect it. In response to the pressures put on him by adults to become more socialized, he has achieved partial control over bowel and bladder functions and over his impulses to act immediately upon his own desires; his wish to please the adults helps him give up some of his own desires in return for their approval. He has developed a keen awareness of the mothering person whose presence comforts him and whose absence, for any prolonged period, upsets him. His attachments to the familiar people have grown from the nonspecific attachment of the very young baby to one in which the familiar adults have great importance for him; he loves them as specific individuals. At the same time, he has become more aware of himself as a separate person and knows something about his own capacities for independent action and feeling.

Often, he has an attitude of complete trust in the adult; at other times, he acts as though he feels himself the victim of an unfriendly and unjust world. At one moment he is affectionate, loving, and approving of the adult; at another, he is demanding and shows his anger and aggression if he is crossed or displeased. Sometimes he wants what he wants intensely, but at other times he can be remarkably loving and giving.

Our goal is not to make of the infant a puppet that automatically obeys our commands. Children can be made into puppets by repeated, strong, and punishing demands for conformity. Instead, we want to lead him toward establishing within himself controls and patterns of behavior. This requires of the adult an ability to respect and value the child's developing as a person in his own right, and the unfolding of his emotional life with its combination of positive and negative expression. It also requires that the adult be available to the child as a communicative partner in affection and interest and, at the same time, as the one who sets reasonable limits, stops trouble, recognizes illness or signs of fatigue, and makes clear what is approved and what is forbidden. These qualities in the adult are of importance in the child's life at any age, but they require special emphasis in the second year, because of the characteristics of that phase of development in the child.

CHAPTER THREE

Activity and Motor Development

He Uses His Motor Skills . . . By the time he is 2 years old, a child can walk in a well-organized manner with the heel-toe progression, and with a beginning rhythmical swinging of each arm. He can climb on a couch or adult chair; he can throw a ball, seat himself in a small chair, and squat on the floor. His hands serve him well in exploring and dealing with his environment. If he is developing in a healthy manner, he uses his motor skills in a variety of ways: he walks from one room to another to find his mother; he climbs on a chair to reach a cookie in the kitchen cabinet; he fits together the pieces of a simple puzzle or toy; he turns to meet a familiar adult; he throws things, either in play or in anger; he jumps with excitement and runs for the joy of running; he pushes away the adult's hand or moves away if something dis-

. . . To Explore agreeable is about to be done; he conducts his own research about sizes, shapes, textures, and other things in the physical world as he piles blocks, fills and empties cups, walks on the sand, and so on. We can put it this way: In a child's motor activity we can see how the ongoing maturation has made certain skills possible to achieve and how the developing skills are organized into action units and syn-

. . . To Express Himself chronized with others. We can also see how motor activity is used to express feelings and to relieve tension.

We will now return to the newborn infant and trace the development of some of the achievements described above.

Much of the muscle activity of the newborn baby is diffuse and random; he flails his arms, wriggles, and kicks. Yet some of his activity is already organized into patterns that serve survival. For example, at birth a baby has re-

...To Eat flexes that orient him to feeding: if the area around his lips and cheeks is touched lightly, he turns his head toward that side, the tongue moves toward the stimulus, and sucking movements occur. But, at this age, we do not believe that he "thinks" about this, or that it is under his control.

...To Look The first set of muscles over which the infant gains control are those of the eyes. During his first three months, he develops the ability to focus on and follow objects with his eyes, that is, he learns to look. This is an active ability: he will turn his head and, a few weeks later, will change the position of his body in order to look at people or things or his own hand.

Between 3 and 4 months of age, he is able to clasp his hands together while lying on his back. From this time on, he increasingly uses his hands to touch, grasp, explore, and control. By the time he is 6 or 7 months old, he has gained control over the muscles that support his head and

...To Explore move his arms. His head is held erect and steady; he can
His Body reach out with one hand to pick up a toy; he can bang it and pass it from one hand to the other; he can easily get his thumb to his mouth; he can reach his toes and all other parts of his body. He can hold on tightly to something he wants. He can roll over from back to front and

...To Control back again, and can keep his trunk erect when placed in a
His Body chair with some support.

At this time, he can support much of his weight if placed in a standing position, and can bounce up and down, but

he does not pull to stand on his own until around 9 months.

... To Sit and Creep

By 9 months also, he will have learned to creep on hands and knees after a few weeks of crawling or pivoting on his belly. He waves his hands or claps them together in the bye-bye and pat-a-cake games. He holds out a toy, takes it back, drops it on purpose, or throws it.

His World Expands ...

The skill in creeping increases steadily so that by the end of the first year a child may creep rapidly about the house or yard. This brings him into more and more contact with the world of things. It is not difficult to imagine how much larger the world quickly becomes for him. This, of course, is furthered also by the baby's learning to walk upright, which comes at the end of the first year or shortly thereafter. At the same time he has developed great precision in control of his arms and hands; he can pick up tiny objects, such as crumbs or bits of fuzz, with ease. He uses his forefinger to poke into things and, a bit later, to point to what he wants.

The baby's ability to go to something he wants or away from something he does not want gives him an important means of increasing learning, of satisfying his wishes, and of defending himself against real or imagined enemies. Perhaps these sound like mature traits for an infant, but we are talking about the early phases of a most important process. The infant, we say, "turns active" toward the end of the first year. This is easily seen in the motor sphere,

... Socially and Emotionally

but it occurs in his social and emotional development also. We believe that this process is of great importance in his being able to grow up, master successive developmental tasks, and cope with difficulties both in his inner (mental) life and in the outside world.

The toddler, as we often call the 1- to 2-year-old, is both a delightful and exasperating creature: delightful because of the many things he does to communicate with us, and because of the pleasure we have in his achievements and his increasingly complicated personality; exasperating because we do not find it easy to understand his moods, feelings, and intentions, and because he is not as willing as the younger infant was to let us run the show.

... As Well As Physically

He Learns To Walk

Early in the second year, the big event is the infant's learning to walk alone. In our society, this occurs for most infants between 11 and 13 months. At first, the infant walks with feet wide apart, and with frequent starts and stops. He falls forward, or often backward, by sitting down suddenly. He stands up and begins again, usually holding his arms out from his side and partly up in the air, with his hands at shoulder height to help maintain balance. We have only to observe him to be impressed with how he works at this and how much pleasure he gets from it.

He Begins To Run and Climb

By the time the child is 18 months old, he walks well and runs a little. He can negotiate a step up or down to get from one room to another. He can back up to a low chair and seat himself and can climb on the sofa. He may become an ardent chair or table pusher for a while. During the next few months, the walking becomes increasingly well organized and smooth; he walks with feet closer together, and the heel of the forward foot touches the surface as the back foot is raised on the toes. The length of his step and the timing are more regular. He begins to swing his arms in time with the stepping. Later the act of walking will become much more automatic, but in the 2-year-old it is still deliberate and involves much energy and intent.

He Needs Protection

With all these motor skills that the 2-year-old now has, he can get into dangerous situations: The stove, the high place, the bottles under the kitchen sink, and the street are a few of the common things and places that may become dangers. Since we know that he can learn only gradually what is safe and what is dangerous in our complicated world, he must have protection. At this age, he has more ability to get into trouble through his motor skills than knowledge to stay away from it.

Summary The 2-year-old's movement toward and away from things and people, his use of his hands in making contact and exploring things, his mastery of walking in the upright position all play an important part in his learning. Independent walking is also important in his developing awareness of himself as a person distinct from others. His body and hand skills not only serve his learning and the mastery of steps in development, but are also used to express his feelings: changes in activity accompany excitement, fear, pleasure, anger, or distress; often, without fully realizing it, we "read" this language of behavior.

We can support and facilitate the motor development of the infant in the following ways:

.. We can provide physical contact and social contact that serve as a stimulus to him to use his muscles.

.. We can provide him with toys and other objects appropriate to his age to look at, listen to, touch, grasp, and manipulate.

.. We can provide him with opportunities to use and practice the skills he is developing. These opportunities range from letting him splash in the bathtub to letting him creep, walk, climb, feed himself, and give vent to his anger in some appropriate way.

.. We can provide him with protection and limits. This means helping him when something is too difficult; it means providing him with a safe place to play; it means taking him out of dangerous spots; it means saying "no" firmly and definitely when "no" is necessary. In doing these things, we make practical use of what we know about what he can be expected to do and to understand.

CHAPTER FOUR

The Development of the
Sense of Self

The development of a sense of the self as an individual is gradual and extends over many years. It is complicated and includes many steps, starting with the infant's awareness of his body, and proceeding to the adult's sense of self-esteem and of a personal and social identity.

When we speak of identity here we mean the child's knowledge of himself as someone who is the same person yesterday, today, and tomorrow—even when there are changes in where he is or what he can do. It includes his knowledge that others recognize his sameness and continuity. He also gradually learns, through the way in which he is cared for, trained, and educated, that he is a part of a larger group that has certain customs, values, requirements, and goals. Some of the factors and steps in this development are worth attention because they increase our understanding of the child and of how he grows into a person who is both like others and unique.

The Beginnings The first step for the infant is learning to know his body self. It seems likely that from his earliest days, his eyes play an important role in the beginning of his perception of himself, as he begins to inspect parts of his own body. The hand also plays an important role through its function in hand-mouth activity and in touching parts of the body. Experiences in self-stimulation, which are added to the experiences of being touched, moved, and handled by the adult, are believed to contribute important components to the child's knowledge of the boundaries of his own body and his dawning awareness of himself as separate from the mothering person.

Self-Discovery and Self-Stimulation

Some of these steps in self-stimulation are easily observed. At about 4 months, a baby is able to clasp his hands together and to play with them. Adults seeing this say the baby has "found" his hands, because it looks like an act of discovery as well as an achievement in grasping. By 4 to 5 months, the mouth-hand contact is well established; the baby can consistently and intentionally get his thumb to his mouth and suck it. As his ability to approach and grasp and touch becomes better developed through maturation, the infant can touch all parts of his body. He reaches and feels his feet and toes by 5 to 6 months, having discovered his knees a little earlier. By 6 to 7 months, he lifts his feet to his mouth and sucks his toes with signs of pleasure. He finds the genital area in what appears at first to be an accidental manner, and slightly later apparently under the combined influences of maturation and the pleasurable sensations that accompany the touching, he finds and explores this area at will.

Signs of Growing Awareness

Toward the end of the first year he does many things that seem to reflect his growing awareness of his own body: He rolls, creeps, and manipulates toys; he sucks his thumb, mouths his hand and fingers, pinches his belly, tugs at his ear, pulls or sucks his toes, pokes into his navel, strokes his cheeks or lips, clasps his hands, rubs his feet together, and so on. It appears that through these actions the baby is learning much more about the boundaries of his body and what he can do with it.

*Awareness of the
Mental Self*

Along with this learning about his body, the infant also begins to develop an awareness of his personality; the self that is not simply a body self is developing. Several things are seen toward the end of the first year that seem to reflect this developing consciousness of his mental self. His anxiety at his mother's disappearance and his realization that she can be brought back when he calls seem to indicate that he has some knowledge of separateness. His learning to use specific names for parent, bottle, and other objects and the anticipation of what happens in a peek-a-boo game when he takes the initiative in starting it illustrate some parts of this process.

*Awareness of
Others*

In the second year, the baby distinguishes family or group members by name and is increasingly aware that they are different from one another and from himself. He has a name for himself, which he can use appropriately. By the end of the second year, his understanding of the pronouns me and you is another sign of his awareness of himself and others. He begins to assign ownership to various objects, for example, your hat, mommy's purse, my cookie, my daddy. He reveals some of his knowledge by his ability to find parts of his body and to know that they are different from those of other people. All of these things are aspects of the development of his image of himself as a person.

Through his individual development and his place in the family or group, he builds up a picture of who and what he is, what he can do, and what he feels and thinks. The process continues and undergoes modification over many years as growth and experience proceed.

*The Sense of
Self in Infants
Without Families*

A group living situation, in which there are several caretakers and frequent changes in the environment, is quite different from a stable family. It is to be expected therefore, that there would be differences in the development of the sense of self and a personal identity for infants growing up in a situation unlike that in a family.

How might group living affect the development of the sense of self? It is probable that the earliest phase, developing knowledge of the body self, would not differ from that of the child reared by his own mother, as long as the child reared in the group has care that is geared to his individual needs. The earliest phases of the mental awareness of his own person should also be quite normal as long as he has enough personalized care to help him form a specific attachment. He can gradually learn to value himself, and later others, if he has been valued by the adults who care for him. If he remains with the same adults and children over long periods of time, he has a good chance to form personal attachments with them and to feel himself a part of a relatively stable social group whose members have specific roles, even though this experience might differ from that of a family-reared child.

But if adults and children are frequently changing, his sense of self and his personal identity will suffer because he does not have the constancy of relationships within which to develop them. In such situations, what security and sense of belonging he develops may be mainly tied to the physical environment and the daily routines. This is an undesirable situation: among other detrimental effects, it stunts the child's emotional development and his ability to develop a sense of self; and it may interfere with his capacity to act as a parent and form a stable family of his own. We cannot afford to believe that we are caring for infants in a favorable way unless there is some continuity and constancy in the people who care for them.

CHAPTER FIVE

The Development of Play

Playful activity is a prominent and important aspect of a child's development. All of us accept play as a natural part of childhood and become worried about a child who does not or cannot play. There are good reasons for this concern: The child who cannot play is a child in trouble.

Play Has Many Functions Play is one of the avenues through which the child develops an understanding of the real world and learns how to make his way in it. We usually associate play with pleasure, but it is often quite serious; in his play, the child may be working out problems and anxieties as well as having enjoyment. Play is also a means through which he begins to understand the roles of others; he imitates his parents and later plays at being one person or another.

It is useful to us, then, in trying to understand the infant to consider his play, how it develops, its importance in his life, and what it tells us about him. A study of a child's play reveals much about his intellectual and emotional development.

Early Phases The first steps in the development of play are stimulated by the social interchange between infant and adult; infants who are deprived of such stimulation do not become normally playful. The first toys that are given are usually things like a rattle, a "cradle gym," or "nursery birds" that are suspended over the crib for the baby to look at and later to reach out and grasp. But the earliest playthings can be said to be parts of his own body or of that of the mothering person.

The First Playthings

Play with his own body, play with toys, and social play with the adult go along together in the first year. The infant of 4 months plays with his hands, and a little later with his feet. During the first 6 months he gradually develops the ability to reach out and grasp a toy which he mouths, bangs, looks at, and manipulates with increasing skill.

He Inspects and Combines

By 9 months the infant shows an ability to handle more than one toy at a time, demonstrating this in such actions as banging two toys together or putting a toy inside a box or cup. By this time also, he examines them more carefully, inspecting them with his eyes and poking into them with his fingers. We call this "exploratory interest"; it shows the development of the ability to distinguish small details. He can now remember a toy long enough to find it when it is covered, and this tells us something about his mental growth too: He has begun to be able to remember and to know that things exist even when they are out of sight. Also, he is now likely to have strong preferences for one toy over another and may object strenuously if the toy he wants is taken away from him.

He Remembers

Development of Preferences

The Social Partner

His play with the adult also goes through various stages. Beginning with the early smiling and cooing in response to stimulation, he soon initiates a social contact; that is, he does not always wait for another person to make a contact, but starts it himself by smiling, making a vocal signal, or reaching out with his hands to touch or tug. He begins to play such games as peek-a-boo, so-big, and bye-bye with great glee at around 8 or 9 months; shortly, he develops other tricks that he repeats for the pleasure of a response from others. At about the same time that he begins to explore the toys, he pokes into the nose, mouth, or eyes of the adult while he is being held, appearing both curious and playful. His laughter, his first words, and many other sounds also become part of a playful interchange with others and may be repeated, though for his own pleasure when he is alone.

Play Reflects His Maturation

In the second year, the baby's play becomes increasingly complex and reflects his rhythms, interests, and maturation. In the first half of the second year, he learns to roll or toss a ball, he fills and empties cups, he begins to pile blocks, and he enjoys messing in water or mud and playing in the sand. After he has learned to walk he enjoys pulling or pushing a toy or the furniture. He enjoys "finding" his nose, eyes, ears, and so on, at the adult's request; he also enjoys other games that use his own body, such as "this little piggie." He is likely to be interested in the pots and pans, the cans of food, the kitchen utensils, and the broom or vacuum cleaner. At this age, other objects belonging to adults, such as hat, shoes, pipe, or purse may be more interesting to him than his toys.

Fantasy Play and Imitation

Beginning about the middle of the second year, we see signs of early fantasy play that is, at this time, largely an imitation of what he has seen or what has been done to him. He hugs a doll or teddy bear and feeds it, puts it to bed, talks to it lovingly, or scolds and spanks it. He puts on shoes or a hat that belong to an adult and swaggers around. He imitates the sweeping, dusting, or dishwashing. In some of this play, we see the beginnings of a process through which he identifies himself with the adults and begins to assume some of their characteristics and behavior.

Solitary and Parallel Play

For the most part, he plays alone or with the adult. If there are other toddlers around, he will be quite aware of them and they may play alongside each other, with occasional periods of contact, but true cooperative play comes only later. There is no doubt that children of this age are interested in each other, but not yet as real partners in play.

Simple games that involve run-and-chase and hide-and-seek are often initiated with the adult, or at times with another child. As motor skills develop further, the child climbs, jumps, and runs. A rocking horse or swing is enjoyed for its contribution to his pleasure in repetitive rhythmical activity.

As was said in the beginning, much of the play is exuberant and joyful; some of it is serious; sometimes elements of anxiety or anger are clearly visible; at times it appears quiet and thoughtful; at other times effortful or exciting. The child learns, lives part of his life, expresses his feelings, and masters many developmental tasks through his play.

Role of the Adult

The adult is important in the earliest phases of the child's play as the social partner who helps it develop. Without reasonably good care and the interest of the adult, infants do not become playful. The adult also provides toys and playthings, as well as opportunities to use them. In the child's second year, the adult continues, part of the time, to be a playmate who responds to the child's playfulness and contributes some of the play ideas. But she also sees to it that the child has some time to play in his own way, in a safe environment. During their first two years, children are not capable of cooperative play with others. It is not appropriate to their needs, therefore, to try to organize play groups for them. A toddler may enjoy playing in the vicinity of other toddlers or older children, but he must be carefully supervised by an adult.

CHAPTER SIX

The Development of Speech and Thought

Begins To Learn To Speak The ability to speak is a complicated function of crucial importance in human development. Early in life its development can be disturbed by various kinds of adversity. Lewis, who has made an extensive study of the language development of infants, has introduced the question about the development of language in infants as follows: "When does a child begin to learn to speak? The answer is, if not at the moment of birth, then certainly during the first day. For as soon as a child cries and someone pays attention to his cry, the first step has been taken; the essentials of language are there: one person makes a sound which another interprets."[1] Lewis' description is an especially useful one because it emphasizes the crucial role of the responsive adult in the development of the child's ability to speak.

The earliest phases of what will later be speech are the spontaneous and responsive vocalizations and vocal signals of the infant. The earliest not-crying vocalizations (first month) are throaty noises and gurgling sounds. In the *Social Vocalization* second and third month, he produces delightful musical cooing in response to being talked to by the adult. He de-

1. M. M. Lewis, *How Children Learn to Speak* (New York: Basic Books, 1959), p. 14.

velops a chuckle and by the fourth month a real belly laugh. By the time he is 5 months of age, he has greatly enlarged his inventory of sounds to range from a high-pitched squeal to a low-pitched growl, and he uses all these sounds to initiate a social contact with the adult. He also will vocalize when alone, as though talking to his toys, to his hands, or for his own amusement. This is a period, before he has begun to react to strangers, when he is likely to be responsive to anyone who shows an interest in him and delights every adult with his babbling.

By 6 and 7 months, there are clearly enunciated consonants and vowel syllables. The ma and da sounds are heard now, and at around 8 months, as maturation proceeds, these sounds are extended and combined to form the mama and dada sounds. When these sounds first appear they are not names; the baby is not yet that specific. But in the last part of the first year, they become names because the adults respond as though they were names: they show pleasure, they repeat the sounds, they associate the sounds with themselves, and soon the infant gets the idea. Mama becomes the name for mother, dada for father, perhaps also *First Words* baba for bottle, and nana for grandmother. This is an example of one way in which the baby learns from adults; it demonstrates how necessary their responses are.

By the end of the first year the infant can make all the basic sounds he will need for speech, and he also has two or three words in his vocabulary. He can recognize a number of everyday objects when they are named for him (bottle, light, cup, car, for example). He can imitate the greeting "hi" or the cautionary "hot" or "no-no."

Jargon Soon after his first birthday, he begins to use jargon, or to jabber. This is a delightful period when he talks in long sentences with much expression, but in an unknown tongue. This jargon provides the melody and phrasing to

Words Are Combined

his speech. At the same time, he is learning more and more single words. By 18 months, he has at least 20 words in his vocabulary and combines them into short phrases such as "daddy come," "go night-night," and so on. He can recognize and name familiar objects in pictures. This, too,

Words and Pictures Are Combined

is a big achievement; it shows that he can make a connection between a real object and its picture—indicating further growth in his mental ability. In the last 6 months of the second year, words are added to his vocabulary at a rapid rate; by the age of 2, some children have as many as

Words Are Combined into Sentences

50 to 60 words. The child can now speak in short sentences, using pronouns; he knows the names of people and things. He can use his speech to ask for what he wants ("I want a cookie" or "give it to me"); to register a protest ("I don't like you"); to express his delight ("daddy's coming"); to commend himself for good behavior ("wee-wee, good boy"); or to express his anxiety ("mommy not go"). He can ask and answer simple questions.

The child's speech will become steadily more complicated and will increasingly serve him in his social relationships. It also can be said that the child communicates

Inner Language and Thought

not only with others, but with himself as well. He develops an inner language that is part of the ability to think. With the development of speech, he moves toward the more complicated system that leads to logical and ordered thinking.

The speech of the adult to the child is very important not only for his speech development, but for many other reasons as well. From the person who talks to him, the

The Speech of the Adult

infant hears much about himself and his world. Things, feelings, actions, and people are labeled for him. There is often much mutual imitation between adult and infant that further stimulates the infant's speech and is a great pleasure for the adult as well. The speech of the adult is also one of the ways in which feelings are communicated.

In his early infancy, the child responds not so much to the specific words as to the tone of voice and the expressions of the adult. Later he begins to realize that certain words have certain specific meanings, and he begins to understand and to use them. Much is communicated, of course, without words; these nonverbal communications are important too, but as a child grows he needs more and more verbal communication.

Summary   Infants must be talked to. The speech of the adult is one of the most important carriers of feelings and of information, and it helps to stimulate and organize the infant's language and thought.

One of the shortcomings of many group care settings has been that adults have not talked enough with young children. Talking at them—giving orders, for example—is not enough. If we wish to teach a child about his world, about himself, and about other people, we must talk with him. This means that the adult must have the time and interest to know the individual child, to speak with him, to listen to and to respond to his communications.

CHAPTER SEVEN

Providing a Favorable
Environment for Infants

Adults Must
Provide

As we have seen, the infant begins to interact with his environment from the moment of birth, and one of the important functions of the adult is to control, mediate, and interpret the environment so that the infant receives stimulation with protection. We will speak here of general principles and some of the more obvious ways in which the most important elements of the infant's world can be provided. We can condense this as follows: Adults must provide (1) things and experiences, (2) information about them, (3) opportunity for action, and (4) the human relationship that is necessary to the development of interest and motivation, that is, the "energizing" influence.

In early infancy most of the child's introduction to the world of things and people comes about through the routines of care. In the feeding, diaper changing, and bathing situations, the infant encounters not only the person but things (bottles, shirts, and diapers, for example) that take on meaning for him as part of the satisfaction of his bodily needs. We also introduce toys for him to look at, grasp, or mouth, and we bring these to him before he is expected to do much with them. The simple, natural activity of the adult in showing a baby a rattle or some other toy makes the toy a part of the baby's world and promotes his interest in it. Safe, attractive toys can be placed above or in his crib from early infancy.

This stimulation should be provided within a protective atmosphere. It is important that the infant have a relatively peaceful place to sleep; when he is awake, it is not good for him to be constantly in the center of an active, busy household. We expect to tone down some of the sights, sounds, and other stimuli in order to provide the infant with a favorable atmosphere in which to grow and develop his perceptions of the outside world and his ties to it.

Stimulation with Protection

Not only the infant but the toddler and also the older child need to have times of respite from involvement with people and activities, both for the rest it provides and for the chance it gives him to become aware of and to organize his inner life. In general, children who are crowded into homes or shelters or who live in other situations where there is never an opportunity to be alone except during sleep, tend to be more excitable, less aware of their own abilities, and more exclusively dependent upon the physical presence of others for their security than those who are provided with opportunities to learn to enjoy being alone part of the time. A favorable environment for the growing child will include such moments of peace.

Peaceful Moments

Overstimulation, however, is not usually the most frequent problem in group care. The problem is in the other direction—that of providing enough stimulation. It is this consideration to which we must pay particular attention, expecially when an adult has many children to care for in a group setting and when several caretakers are involved with each child for parts of a 24-hour period.

The crucial nature of what is done by the person who cares for the infant cannot be overstated. The infant must

The Personal Factor receive a certain amount of personalized care before he will develop the ability to play; he must receive a certain amount of physical handling in order to develop the ability to sit, creep, and walk at the expected time; he must have people talk to him in order to develop normal speech; he must have someone who communicates what is safe and what is dangerous in order to develop an awareness of these things; he must have a person who cares for his body and communicates interest and information before he can develop a sense of himself as a person; he must have people who love and value him if he is to love and value himself and others.

There should also be variety and change in what the infant can see, hear, and feel. This means, for example, after *Variety and Change* he is a few weeks old he should not spend all his time in one room or even in the house. Being out-of-doors in the fresh air for some time each day has long been recommended as a health measure. Today it is probably even more important as a way of enlarging the infant's world. When he is very young he will, of course, not do much except watch the changing scenery and feel the contrasts and changes in light, movement, temperature, sound, and smells. Later, as his abilities increase and he can creep or walk, he makes his own contact with a variety of things and activities that are part of the outdoors.

Variety and contrast are provided in other ways too. The smell, tastes, textures of his food, and the implements that are used in feeding vary. He is permitted to explore with his mouth or bite upon some nonedible but safe objects, such as toys or his own thumb. Before he can sit alone, he is propped up for brief periods or held upright. This gives him another view of the world. When he can sit alone he is placed in a high chair for feeding.

Being taken to the grocery store or drug store or to an-

The Richness of Ordinary Experiences

other house or for a ride in the car are a few of the more ordinary excursions to which the infant should be introduced and from which he will gradually learn. These are events that the child in a family will normally experience in the course of daily living because his parents will often take him along when they visit or shop, out of choice or of necessity. These ordinary experiences are important to the child's learning about the world, and if such experiences are not automatically a part of his life, they should be arranged. It is no service to the child to leave him in the small world of the nursery all day; he needs to participate in the lives and activities of others.

Opportunities for Action

The infant spends part of his time in a playpen or out on the floor. When he can creep and walk, he must be provided with opportunities for doing so. He is allowed to touch, handle, and manipulate things that are safe for him. At the same time, things that are unsafe are removed from his hands or mouth and he is cautioned about them; he is removed from dangerous places. The very process of doing things serves a number of important functions: It increases learning in general; it provides an avenue for the discharge of feelings; it promotes the development of specific skills; it is necessary to the infant's development of an awareness of himself and what he can do.

The Harmony of Development

It is worth remembering that the infant can understand the meaning of "no-no" at about the same time as he is curious enough to explore and mobile enough to get into things that might be dangerous to him or objectionable to the adult. In this respect, we see one of the reassuring facts about the well-cared-for, normally developing child: his ability and willingness to respond to the limits set by the adult go hand in hand with his increasing curiosity and independence.

More Toys and Play

As the child grows into the second year, both the toys and the experiences become more complicated as we continue to provide things appropriate to his stage of development. We provide toys that he can fill and empty, blocks to pile, a ball to throw or kick, a toy to pull or push as he walks. He also needs things that he can be allowed to pound or bite, and a doll he can cuddle, care for, or spank. At times, sand, water, dough, or clay to dig, feel, and mess in should be available to him. Toys and equipment that support gross motor activity, such as a small kiddie-car or rocking horse, and places where he can be allowed to climb or run with some freedom are important.

Books and Music

Pictures to look at and to identify are provided in books and magazines; music to jump and dance and listen to is easily introduced through musical toys that the toddler can manipulate himself or through records, radio, or television. Another enriching experience for the infant is hearing the adult sing. It doesn't matter whether she sings a lullaby, a nursery rhyme, a hymn, or a rock 'n' roll song. If she is singing to him, her singing has value as a social experience; if she is singing to herself as she goes about her work—whether happy, pensive, or sad—it helps the infant to learn to recognize something about the feelings and moods of another person.

Making the Physical Environment Safe

There are some fairly common dangers in the physical environment, too, that the infant must learn to know. Before he is able to creep or walk, one of the main things is to be sure that the playthings we allow him to have are safe. For example, toys, furniture, and window ledges that the infant might chew on must be painted with lead-free paint. Toys that the young infant is given should be larger than his mouth and have no small, removable parts that he could swallow or choke on. His crib should be free of cords or string in which he might become entangled. Beads, buttons, pins, and sharp objects should be kept out of his reach.

A young infant should not be left alone on a dressing table, bed, or couch without something to prevent his falling. In the car, a safety strap, a car seat, and later a seat belt are important. As he gets a little older and begins to walk or move, the fireplace, radiator, heater, or hot air register should be screened off. The kitchen stove is especially fascinating to a toddler. The handles of pots should be kept out of his reach. Since there is no practical way to erect a barrier, the toddler must be taught to stay away from the stove. Barriers may be quite useful in other places—at the top of the stairs, or between one room and another, or whenever it is necessary to confine the child to one area. Since many of the commonly used household cleaning materials contain poisons, they must be kept out of his reach. Obviously, the same is true of medicines and cosmetics. Electric outlets should have safety covers; electrical appliances such as coffee pots, irons, and vaporizers should be placed out of reach.

A child under 2 years of age should not be left alone in a bathtub or wading pool, even for an instant, or near the street or unguarded stairs. All play areas in which the child is left unattended should have barriers and contain only safe pieces of equipment.

Even though he may have learned to avoid the stove or the street when the adult is present, he cannot be trusted alone, for he has no real judgment, and anything that looks attractive to him can lead him into danger.

These precautions are necessary in providing a safe environment, but they should not be taken to mean that the infant should be kept in cotton batting. We should make the surroundings as safe as is realistic with daily living, allow the child as much freedom as is safe, and be responsible for helping him learn the limits and the dangers.

Summary   By providing a personal relationship, a world of things and experiences, information about them and opportunity to make use of them, we promote the healthy growth and development of the infant. We work to establish a favorable balance of routine and variety, sameness and contrast, protection and freedom, and we stand to be reasonably successful because the human baby is remarkably adaptable and has certain inborn capacities that make our role easier. His ability to respond also makes it a pleasure to work with him, and thus he gives to us, just as we give to him.

CHAPTER EIGHT

Feeding

Feeding is important not only because it provides essential nutriments for the child's health and growth, but also because it is one of the regular events of his life around which many important contacts with people and many learning experiences occur. The question then is how to feed an infant in a way that helps him derive the most benefit from the experience.

Holding the Baby Most babies should be held to be fed. The person who feeds him should sit in a comfortable chair so that she can relax and cradle the baby in her arms. (If a baby seems tense or startles easily, he will probably feed better if his legs and the lower part of his body are wrapped snuggly in a light blanket.) Milk, which should be warmed to body temperature, may be tested by dropping it on the wrist. The milk should not stream forth from the bottle, but should drop easily.

He Adapts and Cooperates When the nipple is touched to the baby's cheek or one corner of his mouth, he will turn (because of the rooting reflex)[1] take hold, and begin to suck. Some infants suck

1. The rooting reflex is a name given to an automatic action with which the infant is born that provides that when his cheek is touched or stroked, he will turn his head in that direction and will make searching movements with his mouth.

strongly and steadily with a "no-nonsense" kind of behavior. Some suck a few minutes and rest a few minutes; they often nurse well but take longer to finish. Some become so excited or active that they lose the nipple and begin to cry. These children may need to be calmed down before they can begin to feed again. For most young infants, the feeding will take 20 to 30 minutes, and enough time must be allowed. Some babies "burp" easily and spontaneously after feeding when held in a sitting position or upright on the adult's shoulder. Others are slower and may be helped by gently rubbing or patting the back. At times, most babies will spit up a mouthful of milk after a feeding; they should

Contentment be content when they have finished feeding, though not necessarily ready for sleep.

Solid Foods Physicians differ in their advice about when to start the infant on solid foods (strained or pureed foods). Early starting—around 2 months—is not unusual. Most infants, however, do not need these foods before 3 or 4 months of age. Any new food, when first used, should be given once a day in small amounts.

New Tastes, His first solids introduce the baby to several new experi-
Textures . . . ences. There is a new taste. Some infants seem to prefer some foods to others from the beginning and may be quite definite in their likes and dislikes; others may be ready to take everything that is offered. There is a new consistency. The texture and thickness of the new food is quite different from that of the formula and we believe that this difference is something important for the infant to learn.

. . . and Tools There is a new implement or tool. A small-sized spoon that easily fits into the baby's mouth is needed. The baby meets the spoon and must learn to take his food from that; its feel is different from that of the nipple. There is a new feeding position. When the baby begins to take solids, he should be in a more upright position than when he takes

the bottle, even though he still needs support. This new position is a more wide awake one; he is ready to be more sharply aware of the new tastes, textures, feelings, and what is going on around him. We believe that the feeding of solids should be a learning experience and that is why we do not recommend putting these foods in the bottle to be sucked out as liquids with the milk.

He Starts To Help Himself

By the time he is about 6 months old the baby actively reaches out to pick up or grab something. He can reach out, grasp the bottle, and guide it to his mouth. This new ability means that while being fed he can also reach for the spoon and may object strenuously if not allowed to have it. He can also push the bottle or spoon away when he does not want it. This is a time when the adult may be tempted to pin his arms down so that he cannot get in the way, but this is not a wise thing to do. It is much better to give him something to hold in his own hand—another spoon or a crust of bread—letting him do with it as he will.

Don't Fight Him

He Imitates

One of the things we find ourselves doing with a baby of this age is opening our own mouth as we give him a mouthful of food. This seems to help him to eat because he is old enough now to imitate some of our actions. About this time, too, it is a good idea to introduce him to the cup, not for taking his milk, but for taking small amounts of water or juices. The point of this is not to try to shift him over to a cup, but to give him another new thing that he will gradually learn to use. Many babies do not like the cup if we try to use it in place of the bottle for giving the milk. For the infant at this age, the cup should be a bonus and not a substitute.

He Sits Upright

By 7 or 8 months, the infant can sit well enough to be in a high chair when he takes his solids; it is better for him to sit there than to lie passively in the adult's arms.

At about this time, also, he can feed himself a cookie,

cracker, or bread crust and should be allowed to do so, not because we want him to take over his own feeding, but because by starting with what he can and wants to do, we gradually and slowly help him learn how to do more. He probably will not actually eat much of the hand food at first, but he will inspect the bread, take it to his mouth, suck or bite it, and make some chewing and swallowing movements. He gets better at this with practice, and he is getting much more out of it than just exercising a mechanical skill. We believe that if we encourage activity like this at the proper time, we help the baby to learn gradually that he can do some things for himself. Out of such little things, learned one at a time, we help him to build the sense of himself and what he can do.

Let Him Do Something About the Feeding

Later, around 10 to 12 months, most babies can pick up small bits of food between thumb and index finger. They do this about the same time or shortly after we have begun to give them table food, i.e., unstrained food. This food is often mashed, but usually contains lumps or bits that have to be chewed or mouthed before they can be swallowed. Often the canned foods called Junior Foods are used at this time. Chewing movements are usually pretty well developed by 8 or 9 months, regardless of the baby's number of teeth. The child's activity and participation in the feeding should now be well developed. He should be allowed some finger foods (small bits of meat, vegetables, dry cereal, fruit) to feed himself. He needs to be given a chance to use the spoon, but he still needs the adult to feed him most of his meal and to be with him throughout.

Chewing and Finger Feeding

The period from 12 to 18 months may be most trying for the adults, as far as feeding is concerned, because in this area as in others the child shows both his growing independence and his continued dependence. He can now walk alone, and may fuss when placed in his chair at mealtime.

Trying and Messing

He insists on doing part of the feeding himself, and yet the meal cannot be turned over to him to manage single-handedly. By 12 months he has learned how to throw things, and some of the food and utensils will go on the floor. Messing in things is now a special delight for him. He may also have developed definite ideas about what food he likes and dislikes.

Avoiding Extremes Self-feeding is apt to be a mixture of spoon feeding, hand feeding and cup feeding. Shortly after 12 months, he can use a cup quite well, lifting it accurately to his mouth. He works with the spoon with increasing success and by about 18 months is reasonably skillful with it. For many adults, the combination of independence with messiness and the need for some help is hard to take and mistakes may be made in two directions—either by insisting on feeding the child entirely, or by expecting him to do it all himself. The first extreme is not good for him because it keeps him too babyish and passive; the second is not good for him because it expects far too much and puts a strain on his capacities.

By 21 to 24 months, babies who have been allowed to use their abilities and who have had a good feeding experience will usually feed themselves fairly well most of the time. The 2-year-old can sit in his high chair using the tray or the table. He needs a bib, and it is better for everyone if the floor beneath his chair is washable. He should be given small portions of food which can be replenished as needed. The social aspects of sitting at the table with others are important. He hears adult conversation, laughter, and more serious discussions. Some things are said to him, but most of the time he spends looking and listening. At times he may become overexcited or tired, and both conditions interfere with his eating. When such situations occur, they must be handled according to their cause: If upset or overexcited, he can be comforted or helped to calm down; if overtired, he may need rest more than food.

How the Adult Can Help Adults should make an effort to provide pleasant mealtimes. Temporary changes in appetite and variations of interest in eating are to be expected. It is important that the feeding not become a battleground between adult and child.

After eating the solids, when the baby takes his bottle and is in the adult's arms, he may hold her finger or pat the bottle. She may enjoy holding him for a few minutes after the feeding is over before putting him into his crib or playpen. When he is old enough to feed himself a cracker or cookie or to chew on a teething biscuit, he needs to have these provided. The adult may let him have such food to mouth, crumble, or bang as he chooses.

When he is old enough to try to use the spoon himself, he needs the chance to do it—though most of the food may end up in his hair, or on his chin, or on the floor. The art of letting the baby do part of it, while the adult still takes the main responsibility, is not too difficult to achieve; and there is a gradual shift as he becomes more and more adept at feeding himself. The adult's presence to provide a steadying hand on the cup or to supplement the child's efforts to get the food into his mouth is important. After the toddler has begun to feed himself, it is possible to be attentive to him without necessarily being seated with him at every moment. If it is not a group meal, the adult can often be doing something across the room, while watching what is going on as the 1 to 2 year-old eats his meal. A word, a smile, a cautionary "careful" gives the child a feeling of continued interest in him.

Presence of the Adult

Summary To make the feeding experience as helpful as possible, the adult must be with the child in a way that communicates warmth and interest. With a young infant, when the feeding is mostly a quiet time, talking to him or singing softly is good. As he gets older and is taking strained foods, he begins to be more wide awake during eating; then, he needs to hear about what he is doing or eating. It does not matter much what the adult talks about, but it is natural to talk about the here and now, for example: "You're going to have your apple sauce now," or "Isn't that good?" or "Your face is dirty." It is good for the child to be fed by someone who is really paying attention to his reactions. This doesn't mean that she should work him up into such a state that he is too excited to eat, but it does mean that since this is a social time, she should not let it be dull or monotonous for either the baby or herself.

CHAPTER NINE

Bedtime and Sleep

Sleep has its own organization and rhythm. From the beginning, there are individual differences. The infant of a few weeks usually sleeps 16 to 18 hours out of 24, in blocks of time of varying length. The average 2-year-old sleeps about 10 to 12 hours. Some infants sleep more soundly than others. Some establish regular sleep patterns easily, and some only with difficulty.

Providing Good Conditions for Sleep For the infant in the first half of the first year, sleep will usually come if he is physically comfortable—that is, if he is well fed, dry, and has no inner discomfort. The adult provides the opportunity for sleep by putting the child to bed in a reasonably quiet place; then the child's natural rhythms of sleep and wakefulness usually take over. As he grows older, when his mental life becomes more active and complicated and he has more interest in the outside world, getting to sleep may be more difficult and interruptions of sleep more common. Some adults like to hold and rock a baby for a few moments to quiet him; some prefer to give him a bottle in the crib. Some talk in a soft voice or sing a lullaby. Later, reading a story to him may be appropriate. All of these methods can work satisfactorily if the adult is present and creates an atmosphere conducive to sleep.

There are transitional states in which the baby is neither asleep nor awake when he may make various sounds and movements. Anyone who has cared for an infant is accustomed to these periods and learns to respect them: we give the baby time to wake up before we start to do something with him, and we avoid disturbing him when he is drifting off to sleep.

Individual Reactions to Fatigue

When to sleep and rest is a matter that usually cannot be left to the child to decide, because fatigue and the need for sleep do not always mean that the child will want to sleep. Some infants and toddlers, when tired and sleepy, will become "droopy" and fall asleep without any difficulty; others get "wound up" and excited when overtired and have difficulty in relaxing and falling asleep. Insufficient sleep usually makes a child irritable. Although occasional variations in bedtime need not cause trouble, it is well that the toddler have a regular bedtime. Most children will fight sleep at times or resist being put to bed. For some, even in the first year, it appears that the outside world has such an attraction that they do not willingly withdraw from it to go to sleep. Toning down the stimuli in the environment and providing a period of quiet transition may be essential to establishing favorable sleep habits.

Going to Bed Is a Separation

In the second year there are other reasons why going to bed may be resisted. Sleep difficulties are common at the same time that the child's separation anxiety is at its height. Going to bed is, after all, a kind of separation, and some toddlers may resist it out of anxiety. For others, missing the pleasure of being with the adult or with the group arouses a protest. The child may also wake from sleep crying, apparently from some dream that he may not have enough speech to tell about. Or he may wake with physical discomfort from being wet or cold or in pain and finding himself alone, may cry out for the adult.

The child who wakes during the night and cries, needs to be comforted. This does not mean, however, that the adult must rush in immediately. Children can handle small amounts of discomfort and anxiety without becoming panicky. But if the crying persists, or if we sense there is mounting tension or anxiety, the child is in real need of comfort. Often it is enough for him to be spoken to or patted gently. As far as possible, it is a good idea to comfort the child in his own bed. Picking him up or rocking him may be necessary if he is unusually distressed. It is not good policy to offer entertainment or special pleasures, because this stimulation gives him another reason for waking and he then may stay awake for hours while the adult is aching for sleep. If handled properly most sleep difficulties are of brief duration.

The Need for Comfort

Sleep should refresh and replenish the body and mind. In the young child, it is easy to see the change from the irritable and disorganized behavior that accompanies fatigue to the comfort and organized behavior that follow sleep.

Summary

We provide the baby with favorable conditions for sleep, and learn to recognize his individual way of showing fatigue, and the developmental changes as well as everyday occurrences that may result in sleep disturbances. Some regularity in the time of going to bed supports the development of healthy sleep and rest habits, but there should be some flexibility about timing. Infants who live in group care settings are likely to have a regular, if not rigid, bedtime because of the institutional routines. We must be careful to plan so that the individual infant can be responded to in a way that is good for him. This means that he must have individual attention at bedtime and someone to hear his call or cry during the night. Work schedules of those who care for him should be so arranged that he is put to bed by someone with whom he has more than casual contact, and someone who he knows will be available to him if he wakes during the night.

CHAPTER TEN

The Bath, Diapering, and Dressing

We bathe babies, obviously, to keep them clean. Keeping them clean not only prevents skin irritations; it makes them much more attractive and pleasing to us. But our purpose here is to call attention to what the bath contains as an experience for the baby—what stimuli and sensations it involves; what it contains as a social situation; what kind of learning opportunities it affords.

The Setting The setting of the bath is important for reasons of the infant's health and comfort. We are accustomed to bathing the infant in a room that is warm enough for him and in water that is about the same temperature as that of his body. He may be bathed in the sink or in a small tub. It is important also that the arrangement be convenient for the bather. There should be a large enough flat surface on which to place the baby; and the tub should be placed at a comfortable height for the bather. After the baby is undressed, he has a chance to move with the greatest freedom and, for the young infant, the bath may be his most

A Variety of Sensations active time. He experiences a variety of sensations to his skin and musculature as he is undressed, soaped, sponged, placed in the water, removed, and dried. He kicks his feet, flails his arms, and attempts to roll. During the actual bathing, for his protection, he has to be held securely. He may cry if the water is too hot or too cold, if his movements are restricted, if soap gets in his eye, and so on.

As the baby gets a little older and can sit up, there are new experiences. He may grab for the washcloth or soap; he may reach for the water tap and must be protected from the hot water; he may drink the bath water or suck on the washcloth. At this time, he will probably begin to enjoy a suitable bath toy that has the double function of providing him something to play with that stimulates his interest and makes it possible for the bath to proceed. Once able to sit alone securely, he can play with his toys happily while being bathed.

Bath Toys

Toward the end of the first year, as he becomes more curious and is also more imitative, he is likely to want to do at least part of the bathing himself: He gives his face or chest a swipe with the cloth. When shifted to a larger tub or sink, he tries to turn the water taps on and off. He conducts his own experiments in how the soap feels or tastes; he may get it into his eye and be outraged, acting as though the adult somehow has caused the trouble. He shows something of what and how he learns as he pours water from cup to cup, or sails a boat, or holds a floating toy underwater and then watches it bob up as he releases it. He may want to walk up and down the length of the tub, splashing grandly. Some play with the genitals is to be expected as part of his interest in his body and should be treated casually. He may now be less willing to get out of the water, and a little extra time to play is often a good idea as long as the adult is nearby.

For many children, the bath has a generally calming and relaxing effect, even when there has been plenty of activity and excitement in the process. Others may become more wakeful and stimulated by the bath.

*The Bath as
Social Experience*

But what of the bath as a social experience? It is a time when, because an adult must be there, both she and the infant can make the most of it. The general stimulation that comes from handling, body contact, washing, and drying is important in the infant's getting to know and to use his own body. As the adult bathes him, she also smiles, talks to him, or plays little games with him. She cautions him or stops him if he starts to do something dangerous; she talks to him about himself or the water or the soap. As the toddler develops more language, the bath is also a time when he talks. In short, it is a time during which many feelings and communications—verbal and nonverbal—pass between the adult and the baby.

Bathing can be hurried and mechanical, a situation in which an adult gives little of herself, or it can be an excellent opportunity for giving the child something of what he needs.

*Diapering as
an Event*

The changing of diapers begins a few hours after birth and goes on for a long time. It is such a routine and frequent activity that one might wonder what need be said about it. But it seems worth mentioning that this activity, too, provides the infant with another contact with the adult during which she conveys, verbally or nonverbally, comfort and stimulation. In early infancy, the baby may cry when wet or soiled because he becomes cold; it is appropriate to change him at that time. This response to his discomfort,

*A Response
to His Discomfort*

along with other responses, helps him make the connection between his cry and the behavior of the comforting adult that leads him gradually to recognize her.

Diaper changing also involves certain bodily sensations as the infant is lifted, as his skin is cleaned and dried, as the dry diaper is put on him. As he grows older, he will be influenced also by the attitudes and feelings of the person who changes him. Early, these mainly should commu-

nicate gentleness, interest, and comfort. A little later, as
Interest in the infant begins to feel his body and genitals when being
His Body changed, a matter-of-fact treatment of his interest is helpful. A shocked or punishing reaction may well make him
feel he must be ashamed of his body.

In the last half of the second year, if toilet training is
begun, the communication of clear information about what
is wanted is necessary. Letting the child know, without
punishing, that the soiled or wet diaper has become dis-
tasteful is an appropriate reaction (see also Chapter 10 on
Bowel and Bladder Control).

Dressing The infant is undressed or dressed for the purpose of
cleaning him, making him more comfortable, or preparing
him for the next event in the day. Shirts, dresses, buntings,
caps, bibs, sweaters, overalls, snowsuits, and shoes come
and go repeatedly and punctuate his day. At first, as with
other things in his life, they are probably perceived only
vaguely and associated mainly with bodily comfort or discomfort. Later, because of the repetition of various se-
quences of events and because of his own maturation, he
comes to associate them with what is about to happen, that
is, that he is going outdoors, or is going to be fed, or to be
bathed, or to be put to bed. He then begins to show how
he feels about some of the things that he anticipates;
he may be pleased or displeased, happy or unhappy, cooperative or obstructive. As to his abilities and learning,
by the time he is 1 year of age he can cooperate to the extent of pushing an arm through a sleeve or pushing a foot
into a shoe. In the second year, he will usually enjoy pulling off his socks, trying to pull off his pants or shirt, or
putting on his hat. Although he may not be successful at
these tasks, he shows an increasing awareness of the process of dressing and an understanding of which garment
goes where.

Summary   Bathing, dressing, and changing diapers are necessary and ordinary parts of child care. It is important to remember that they are also social and learning experiences for the infant. Every contact that a baby has with another person is meaningful to him. These ordinary experiences, in which there is a transaction between the baby and the adult, are important to his development.

CHAPTER ELEVEN

Bowel and Bladder Control

When the Infant Is Ready In the first year of life, emptying of bowel and bladder is primarily a reflex act that is set in motion by inner stimuli. The young infant has neither the neuromuscular development nor the understanding required to develop conscious control over bowel and bladder functions. The emphasis on very early cleanliness, which leads to the "catching" of stools from infants of a few weeks or a few months, is fortunately less common than it was a few years age. Such early training is more likely to be harmful than helpful and we do not recommend it. Some time in the second year is believed to be the best time to start to help the child achieve bowel control. The exact timing will depend upon some of the factors indicated below, but some time around 18 months is usually a reasonable time to begin.

The Adult's Role and Attitudes The child should be trained by someone with whom he has enough of a relationship that he wants to please her, because the wish to please is one of the reasons why toddlers are motivated to establish control. The adult watches for signs in the child's behavior that he is about to have a bowel movement and takes him to the toilet. Children who are quite regular are usually easier to train because they can be taken to the toilet at a predictable time. In the beginning, the child should not be required to sit more than five or ten minutes, and the adult should stay with him. It is usually best if both the adult and the child keep to the business at hand; therefore, in the early stages, reading stories or providing toys or food may be a distraction rather than a help. When the toddler has had his movement, the adult should let him know that she is pleased. This should be genuine praise that he can recognize, but it should not be exaggerated into great excitement.

Giving Clear Cues   The giving of clear cues to the toddler about bowel training also includes the adults's letting him know that she is displeased when he has his bowel movement in his pants. He should not be punished, but it does no harm to show him that she does not enjoy the smell or the incessant cleaning up.

He should be allowed to see the bowel movement if he wishes, and the child of 18 months is likely to be very interested in it. At first, it is probably best to wait until he is out of the bathroom before flushing the toilet, because the noise and the disappearance of the stool may frighten him. Later he may want to participate in the flushing away. If he wishes to smear or play with the stool, this should be prevented with a clear prohibition, but not punished.

Don't Fight   With toilet training, as with feeding, it is of special importance not to make it a fight. The aim is to join forces with that part of the child that wants to master this developmental task. Toilet training should not become a contest of wills in which the adult forces the child into submission. We believe that for the child's future development it is far better to help him establish his own controls and thus feel more in charge of himself than to make him submit out of fear.

The Child's
Readiness

There are other factors related to the child that are of importance in encouraging bowel control. He should have been walking long enough so that he does not react to sitting on the pot for a few minutes as though it is an unbearable interference with his activity. If he is just beginning to walk he may be so involved in that exercise that he will complain bitterly about sitting even for a few minutes. If so, it is better to defer the training.

His Ability
To Understand

It is important that he have enough words (or enough understanding of them) to associate a simple word or phrase with the bowel movement. These words vary in different families and cultures—"go potty," "make doody," "poo-poo" are some of the usual ones in our society. It does not matter what word or phrase is chosen, as long as there is some consistency in its use. The words help the child to have a more specific knowledge of this function of his body; they also help him understand that he is being asked for something specific. Later he will use the same words to communicate his request to go to the bathroom or to comment on his performance.

His Ability
To Sit
Upright

The seat he uses should be comfortable and secure, since any feeling of uneasiness will interfere with his movement. Some toddlers will be uneasy about heights and will be more comfortable in a low chair that permits their feet to touch the floor. Others will accept a small seat placed over the large toilet seat. It should be small enought to support the child securely, with adequate back and arm rests and a firm foot rest.

Ups and Downs

There will be ups and downs in the process of establishing control. Involvement in play, fatigue, or illness are common causes of toilet "accidents." In many children, there are also periods of resistance to training, which reflect their feelings of protest at a given time. If these are not taken too seriously, they are usually of short duration.

For many children, regularity and control are fairly well organized by age 2; for others it comes somewhat later. There may also be a loss of bowel control (regression) in response to stress of various kinds such as illness, separation from an important person, a change in his life situation, and so on. If this regression continues for a period of weeks or months, it indicates that the child is in need of some kind of professional help.

It should not be expected that toddlers living in groups will be ready or able to control their bowels on a group schedule. It is important to have an individual approach. But it is true that children do some learning by imitation of others, and sometimes the example of another child is a help.

Urinary Control Control of urinary function is usually not difficult to achieve once bowel control is well on the way. It does require that the adult take the child to the toilet often during the day. Timing will depend upon how frequently he wets. It is advisable, at this time, to put him in training pants during the day, because this helps to clarify what is being asked of him. As long as he is in diapers, we are inviting him to use them as he always has, and he can be confused if we ask him to use the toilet and then put him back in diapers.

Summary The achievement of control over bladder and bowel function is a developmental task for the child. Most children are ready to begin this effort some time early in the second year, even though it may be months before it is completed. The adult helps by providing a favorable setting and guiding the child in his efforts. Battles should be avoided; support, consistency, and clear indications of what is expected are important. In group settings there must be the possibility, in this area as in others, of individualizing the care.

CHAPTER TWELVE

Developmental Landmarks

The following pages contain charts showing some of the characteristics of development at various ages during the first two years. Following the charts is an explanation of each item. Most of these developmental characteristics have been described in the text. They are shown in chart form to provide a quick reference to levels and progression of development in five areas:

(1) *Body mastery.* This refers to the development of control over the larger muscles involved in head control, rolling, sitting, creeping, walking, throwing a ball, etc. (see Chapter 3 on Activity and Motor Development).

(2) *Manipulative skills and eye-hand coordination.* This area includes the hand and finger skills involved in grasping and holding things, passing them from one hand to another, and taking things apart. It also includes the coordinated use of the hands and eyes in such skills as piling blocks, scribbling with a crayon on paper, and grasping tiny objects (see Chapter 3).

(3) *Play and the use of toys.* This area traces the development of the child's interest in and use of toys, his grad-

ual awareness that a toy exists even when out of sight, and the beginnings of fantasy play. Feelings about the toys, such as pleasure in them, and displeasure at their loss are part of the picture. Curiosity, memory, and intellectual interest in the qualities of a toy are revealed in some of the steps (see Chapter 5 on The Development of Play).

(4) *Speech.* This area includes the various types of vocalization that lead up to the development of words, vocabulary, and sentence formation. A few items describe the infant's understanding of the language of others, such as the ability to follow directions. The growth of speech implies also the growth of the child's knowledge about other people, about himself, and about his physical environment (see Chapter 6).

(5) *Reactions to others and to self.* Various aspects of the growth of the infant's relationships are included, such as the responsive and spontaneous smile, anxiety to the stranger, social games, and imitation of the adult. The growth of self-awareness and skill in self-care and stages in expression of emotional development, such as affectionate gestures and negativistic behavior, are indicated (see Chapter 2 on Relationships to People and Emotional Growth).

The chart can be read in two ways: one may read across the chart at any level, for example at age 9 months, and find in each of the five areas one more item of development expected at that age. One may also note the steps of development that have been (or will be) taken in any one area by reading from top to bottom, for example, down the Speech column.

It is important to keep in mind, however, that these charts reflect averages or "norms" of development;

not every healthy, normal infant will conform exactly to them. The charts will fit about one-half of the normal infants; about one-fourth of the infants will be advanced, and about one-fourth will lag behind the levels indicated. This fact simply indicates the normal variations we expect in healthy development. But the charts do indicate, in a general way, what kind of development is expected at various ages, and as such can be helpful in understanding the child. Any infant who is markedly below these norms (say by more than two months) will need a careful evaluation to determine the reasons for the delay.

Explanation of Developmental Landmarks Chart

The items that are included in the chart on developmental landmarks are explained briefly below, under the same headings as on the chart.

Body Mastery and Gross Motor Development

In earliest infancy, some body movements are under reflex control and are organized into patterns such as the sucking, rooting, swimming, and startle reactions. Other movements such as kicking, flailing of arms, and wriggling of the body appear diffuse and undirected. As development proceeds, both the reflex movements and the undirected movements are gradually replaced by voluntary movements under the infant's control. Among the first easily seen are the beginning of head control—the infant lifts his head and begins to look around—and the beginning of more active kicking.

Lifts Head High When Lying on Belly (3 to 4 months)

When the infant is lying on his belly, he can lift his head and chest so that he looks straight ahead. Weight can be supported on his forearms or, as he becomes more mature, on his hands.

Rolls, Belly to Back (around 4 months)

The infant can roll from his belly to his back before he can turn from his back to his belly. The action is accomplished mainly by the arms and the trunk with an assist from one leg. A firm surface makes rolling easier.

Supports Head Well When Pulled to a Sitting Position (5 months)

The infant should have enough control of the muscles of his back and neck to keep his head in a straight line with his body as he is pulled from a lying position to a sitting position. Earlier, his head control would not have been good enough to make this possible.

Rolls, Back to Belly (5 to 6 months)

From lying on his back, the infant turns, without assistance, onto his belly. He turns his body, pushes with one leg, controlling his arms so that they do not interfere or get caught under his body.

Sits Alone (8 to 9 months)

The infant can get himself into a sitting position, can sit freely without support and with good control of his head and body. A little earlier (6½ to 7 months), he sits well with support.

Belly Crawl (8 to 9 months)

This is a form of locomotion in which the infant, his belly on a surface, propels himself forward with arm and leg motion. This ability develops before the ability to creep on all fours.

Creeps on All Fours (9 to 10 months)

The infant can get up on hands and knees with body off the surface and move forward by making alternating arm and leg movements. There are several normal variations of creeping.

(Continued following charts)

	Age	Body Mastery	Manipulative Skills and Eye-Hand Coordination
		Movements mostly remain undirected.	Hands partially open or fisted.
		Raises head slightly when lying on belly and looks around briefly.	Grasps voluntarily when toy is placed in hand.
	3 mo.	Kicks actively.	Clasps hands together in play.
		Raises head high when lying on belly.	
		Rolls from belly to back.	Grasps object held near hand.
Some Developmental Landmarks —First Year		Supports head when pulled to sitting position.	Reaches out to grasp block or toy (mitten-like grasp).
	6 mo.	Rolls from back to belly.	Transfers toy from one hand to the other.
		Holds trunk erect when supported in sitting position. Sits alone.	Holds two toys at once.
		Crawls on belly.	
	9 mo.	Creeps on all fours. Pulls self into standing position.	Bangs two toys together.
		Cruises around crib or furniture.	Grasps small object with index finger and thumb (pincer grasp).
	12 mo.	Walks forward with two hands held.	

Play and the Use of Toys	Speech	Reactions to Others and to Self
Looks at toy and follows movements with eyes.	Makes small throaty noises.	Looks at face of adult.
Holds toy (rattle) briefly.	Vocalizes in response to others (musical cooing).	Smiles responsively to people (social smile).
		Alert gaze.
Shows interest in playthings; looks and begins to reach.	Vocalizes spontaneously to self, to people, and to toys.	Distinguishes "mother" from others.
Shows displeasure at loss of toy.	Locates source of sound.	Makes social contact with people by smiling or vocalizing.
		Plays with own foot.
Looks briefly for toy that disappears.	Vocalizes da, ma, ba.	Pushes away something he does not want.
Uncovers toy hidden by cloth.	Vocalizes dada, mama (nonspecific).	Reacts to strangers with anxiety.
Explores toy with eyes and finger (examines and pokes).	Says dada, mama as names.	Enjoys peek-a-boo game.
		Plays pat-a-cake, so-big, and bye-bye.
Shows preference for one toy over another.	Understands "give it to me" and hands toy.	Uses toy to create social contact.
Puts one object inside another.	Has two words besides mama and dada.	Cooperates in dressing.

	Age	Body Mastery	Manipulative Skills and Eye-Hand Coordination
		Walks a few steps alone.	Takes covers from boxes, etc.
		Walks well alone; starts and stops with good control.	Imitates scribbling with crayon.
	15 mo.		
		Climbs stairs on hands and knees.	Turns pages of book two or three at a time.
		Hurls ball.	
	18 mo.	Climbs into adult chair or on couch. Seats self in small chair.	Piles three or four blocks with good coordination.
Some Developmental Landmarks —Second Year			Makes imitative stroke with crayon on paper.
	21 mo.	Squats in play and returns to standing position.	Piles five or six blocks.
		Runs with good coordination.	Turns pages of book one at a time.
		Climbs stairs with aid of rail.	
			Executes circular stroke with crayon.
	24 mo.	Walks up and down stairs alone.	

Play and the Use of Toys	Speech	Reactions to Others and to Self
Finds toy hidden by sofa or behind door.	Repeats familiar words.	Expresses many emotions and recognizes them in others. Rolls ball to another person.
Enjoys "putting in and taking out" game.	Has three to six words besides mama and dada.	Hugs and gives kiss to parent.
	Has elaborate jargon.	May show sharp separation reaction.
Likes pots and pans and other possessions of parents.	Indicates wants by pointing.	Is often negativistic.
Piles three or four blocks.	Has vocabulary of about ten words. Names one or two common objects from pictures.	Identifies several parts of own body.
Recognizes two or three pictures in books.	Follows simple directions.	Handles cup well.
Carries or hugs doll.	Combines two or three words spontaneously.	Tries to put on cap, mittens, etc. Feeds self fairly well with spoon (little spilling).
Explores drawers and cabinets.	Has vocabulary of 20 to 50 words.	
		Imitates adult activities (sweeps, dusts, phones, shaves, reads newspaper, etc.).
Begins fantasy play: takes care of doll or teddy; "goes to store," etc.	Begins to use pronouns I, you, me. Uses three-word sentences.	Likes to please others.

Pulls To Stand *(9 to 10 months)*	Without assistance from another person, the infant gets himself into a standing position by pulling up on furniture.
Walks a Few *Steps Alone* *(12 to 14 months)*	This has been preceded by cruising with support (sidewise stepping) and walking forward with two hands held. Characteristically, the infant taking his first few steps alone, starts and stops and suddenly falls into a sitting position.
Walks Well Alone; *Starts and Stops* *with Control* *(15 to 16 months)*	The gait of the toddler is on a broad base, that is, with feet wide apart, and he now walks well with little falling, unless there is an obstruction.
Climbs Stairs on *Hands and Knees* *(15 months)*	The infant creeps upstairs on all fours. At about the same time, he may learn to descend by backing down or may bounce down the stairs on his buttocks.
Climbs into *Adult Chair* *(18 months)*	He can climb into an adult chair (or often the sofa) without assistance.
Seats Self in *Small Chair* *(18 months)*	The infant has enough body control and enough awareness of himself in space to be able to seat himself in a child's chair.
Squats and Returns *to Standing Position* *(20 to 21 months)*	Body control is good enough that, without need for support, the toddler can squat—often squatting to play for a few moments—and return to standing position.
Runs Well *(20 to 22 months)*	Having become able to walk more and more rapidly, the toddler can now run, swinging his arms in rhythm to his steps.
Walks Up *and Down* *Stairs Alone* *(23 to 25 months)*	This means that the child walks up and down stairs without needing to use the handrail. Characteristically, both feet are placed on the same step. The child usually leads with the same foot for each step. This ability follows his

being able to climb stairs by holding the hand of the adult, or the handrail.

Manipulative Skills and Eye-Hand Coordination

Hands Fisted or Partially Open (1 to 2 months)

This is the typical position of the hands of the infant of 1 month or less. Reflex grasping is present at this time; this means that if one touches the infant's palm with his finger or the handle of a toy, the infant's hand will close around it.

Grasps Voluntarily When Toy Is Placed in Hand (2 to 3 months)

With a little practice, this can be distinguished from reflex grasping, because it has the quality of an intentional act. A toy placed in the infant's hand is held briefly and soon dropped.

Clasps Hands Together in Play (4 months)

This refers to the hand play and mutual hand fingering that becomes possible at around 4 months, when the infant is lying on his back. He clasps his hands together in front of his face or chest. As mentioned in the text, this is often referred to as "finding" his hands.

Grasps Object Held Near Hand (5 months)

Visual attention, interest in the toy, and body control have advanced enough to permit the infant lying on his back to grasp a toy held near (2 or 3 inches away). A few weeks later, he will be able to reach and grasp a toy that is held over the midline of his body.

Reaches Block or Toy (mitten-like grasp) (6 months)

Supported in the sitting position, the infant can approach and pick up a small block on the tabletop. The hand operates with fingers held together as in a mitten, and the grasping is done by the palm contacting the block and fingers closing around it. Later the fingers will be used more skillfully.

Transfers Toy from One Hand to the Other (6 to 7 months)

A block, rattle, or other toy is passed directly from one hand to the other.

Holds Two Toys at Once (7 to 8 months)

The baby is able to pick up a toy and keep it while holding another. This is a further step in the maturation of the motor system. Earlier, he would have had to drop the first toy when he reached for the second.

Bangs Two Toys Together (9 to 10 months)

This is partly a form of play, but also reveals the baby's capacity for more complicated and coordinated use of hands and arms.

Grasps Small Object with Index Finger and Thumb (Pincer Grasp) (10 to 11 months)

The baby picks up tiny objects, such as crumbs and bits of fuzz, with almost adult precision, with his thumb and index finger. The infant's ability to approach and grasp will improve in coordination and refinement, but the basic steps have been taken in the first year.

Takes Covers from Containers (13 to 14 months)

Interest in removing box covers, pulling lids from bottles, and other containers is seen at this time, as well as the manipulative skill required to accomplish it. He may try to put the lids back on, but this is usually more difficult.

Imitates Scribbling with Crayon (13 to 14 months)

The baby will do what he sees the adult do in scribbling with a crayon. He is not imitating the production on the paper but the arm movements of the adult. In doing this, however, he shows a control of his motion and is able, if he wishes, to stay on the paper.

Turns Pages of Book, Two or Three at a Time (15 months)

The child can turn the pages of an ordinary book with fairly heavy pages, two or three at a time. This motor skill coincides with his beginning interest in pictures, but is also enjoyed simply as a motor activity. He turns pages and manipulates the book for the fun of it.

Piles Three or Four Blocks (18 months)	Given a few small blocks and some encouragement, the baby can build a tower three or four blocks high before it topples over. This requires good control over grasping and releasing as well as good eye-hand coordination.
Makes an Imitative Stroke with Crayon on Paper (18 months)	At this time, the baby can control and coordinate his arm, hand, and eye well enough to make a single stroke with the crayon in imitation of the adult.
Piles Five or Six Blocks (21 months)	See above. There is no difference from piling three or four blocks, except for the height of the tower, which reflects the baby's increasing skill.
Turns Pages of Book, One Leaf at a Time (22 to 23 months)	The child can now turn the pages of an ordinary child's book with fairly heavy pages, one at a time. He does this usually by setting his thumb against the edge of the page and pushing. Magazines or books with extremely thin pages are more difficult, of course.
Executes Circular Stroke with Crayon (24 months)	This requires a free and coordinated use of hand, arm, and wrist. The beauty of the circles made is not of concern, but rather the round-and-round stroke.

Play and the Use of Toys

Looks at Toys and Follows Movement with Eyes (1 month)	The infant's visual attention to people and to things in his environment is among the first easily observed developmental achievements. By 4 weeks of age, the infant can focus on an object and follow it with his eyes for a distance about halfway from one side to the other. Naturally, this requires some turning of his head also.
Holds Toy Briefly (2 months)	This indicates a beginning ability to grasp something intentionally rather than by reflex only. It is the same as the "grasps voluntarily" item at 2 months under the Manipulative Skills heading.

Shows Interest in Plaything (4½ to 5 months)

This implies a definite extension of the child's interest, which earlier has been almost exclusively in people. He now should have the capacity to invest the toys with enough interest and attention to encourage manipulation and play. He begins to reach for them and to look at them.

Shows Displeasure at Loss of Toy (6 months)

This reflects the infant's growing interest in playthings and his ability to express protest. He cares enough now about the toy to complain when it is taken away from him.

Looks Briefly for Toy that Disappears (7 months)

Shown here is the baby's beginning awareness that toys (and other things) continue to exist even when they are out of his sight. At this age, when he drops a toy (perhaps while sitting on someone's lap or in a high chair), he looks for it on the floor.

Uncovers Toy Hidden by Cloth (9 months)

This is another interesting step in the baby's mental development. He can now retain a mental picture of something long enough to look for it when it is hidden. This ability increases steadily in the last part of the first year. At this age, however, it is a brief memory of an object that is covered while he is watching. He finds it by taking the cloth away. It is interesting to compare this with the baby's enjoyment of the covering and uncovering of the face in the peek-a-boo game, which occurs about a month earlier.

Explores Objects with Eyes and Finger (10 to 11 months)

The baby now investigates the details of toys and other objects by examining them carefully and poking into them with his index finger. The same kind of exploratory interest is demonstrated in his poking into the mouth or nose or ears of his mother or in fingering the buttons on her clothing.

Shows Preference for One Toy over Another (10 to 11 months)

The baby shows definite preferences for some toys over others and may not so readily accept a substitute as he did earlier. This is followed a short time later by the development of an emotional attachment to a toy, which the child uses to comfort himself and to feel more secure.

Puts One Object Inside Another (11 to 12 months)

This is simply an interest in combining objects that is a part of the baby's early experimentation. Later (at around 13 months), it becomes more active and repetitive.

Finds Toy Hidden by Sofa or Behind Door (12 to 13 months)

This is more complicated than the 9-month item of finding a toy covered by a cloth, and it indicates a further development of memory for the object that is out of sight. At this age, the child keeps the object in mind for a longer time and can make some kind of detour or more complicated action to find it.

Enjoys "Putting In and Taking Out" Games (13 to 14 months)

This refers to the infant's interest in such activities as putting toys into boxes, spoons into pots, and removing them, which he seems to enjoy doing.

Likes Pots and Pans and Other Possessions of Parents (15 to 16 months)

At this period, the child may begin to be more interested in playing with things that belong to adults than with regular child's toys. This goes along with an increasing imitation of the adults' activities described in Reactions to Others and to Self.

Piles Three or Four Blocks (18 months)

The toddler is able to pile several blocks on top of each other, building a tower. The tower gets higher as his coordination and interest grow through the second year.

Recognizes Two or Three Pictures (18 to 20 months)

This refers to the ability to be interested in pictures in a book and the ability either to name or to identify two or three of them.

Carries or Hugs Doll (18 months)

This indicates the very beginning development of interest in a doll (or teddy bear), which later (at around 23 or 24 months) he will be feeding, dressing, spanking, and so on, as his imagination develops.

*Explores Drawers
and Cabinets
(18 to 20 months)*

Beginning at about 18 months and continuing for several months after, the toddler shows particular interest in exploring closets, drawers, and cabinets. This can be most easily observed when he plays freely and indicates by his questions a growing curiosity about the world around him.

*Beginning
Fantasy Play
(24 months)*

The earliest evidences of fantasy or make-believe play in the toddler are imitations of what has been done to and for him, or of other adult activities that he has observed. Feeding, loving, or spanking a doll or teddy bear, or such activities as dusting, mopping, sweeping, going to the store, or acting the part of the milkman, are some of the most frequent forms of such play.

Speech

In the early months, the infant vocalizes mostly in response to being talked to by the adult. Later he vocalizes spontaneously to people, to toys, and to himself.

*Makes Small
Throaty Noises
(1 month or less)*

These are ah-eh-uh sounds that represent the beginning of the infant's expressing himself with his voice without crying.

*Vocalizes
Responsively
to People
(2 months)*

The infant "talks" to the adult, vocalizing a stream of sounds with a musical quality. "Cooing" is the term we use to describe the sounds.

*Vocalizes
Spontaneously
to Himself,
to Toys
(4 to 5 months)*

This is most often heard when the baby is alone, particularly when he is waking up. It has the definite quality of vocalizing for his own amusement—to hear the sound of his own voice, or talking to his hands or to a toy that he is looking at as he has done a little earlier with a person. He uses his voice now also to initiate a social contact.

Localizes Source of Sounds (5½ to 6 months)

This is partially, of course, a test of hearing. It also reflects progress in learning. The infant turns to look at the source of sound. Most babies locate first the sound of another person's voice, but by 5½ to 6 months they turn to other sounds also.

Vocalizes Da, Ma, Ba (7 to 8 months)

These are usually single syllables, produced when the infant is at play with his toys or often when he is interacting with another person. This marks the ability to combine consonants and vowel sounds clearly, which is necessary for developing spoken language.

Vocalizes Dada, Mama (8 to 9 months)

This is nonspecific in that it is not yet associated with particular people. It is an intermediate step and an elaboration of the single syllable da, ma, heard earlier.

Says Dada, Mama as Specific Names (9 to 10 months)

Dada and mama are the first real words, and are attached to people. Names of objects, such as "baba" for bottle, or a greeting such as "hi," may also be heard at this time.

Understands "Give It to Me" and Hands Over Toy (11 to 12 months)

This shows the baby's understanding of the adult's word and gesture in that if someone holds out her hand and asks him for what he has, he will understand the request. This does not necessarily mean that he will give up willingly what he is holding.

Has Two Words Besides Mama, Dada. Repeats Familiar Words (12 to 13 months)

These may be names for more people or objects, greetings such as "hi," or a word denoting action, such as "up." The baby also repeats familiar words or names in an imitative way.

Has Three to Six Words Besides Mama and Dada (14 to 16 months)

The baby's vocabulary grows gradually as more names for objects and actions are acquired; adjectives, such as "hot," "nice," "pretty," taken over from the adult, may be used to designate a danger, such as the stove, or to express pleasure or affection.

Has Elaborate Jargon (15 to 18 months)

Jargon is the name used to describe the delightful flow of nonunderstandable speech produced by the toddler with full inflection and great earnestness. It is precisely as though he were speaking in a foreign language that he understands and others do not. Jargon usually disappears in the latter half of the second year.

Indicates Wants by Pointing (14 to 16 months)

In addition to having a few words, the toddler will communicate what he wants by pointing to it rather than by crying. This ability makes it easier to understand him.

Has Vocabulary of About Ten Words (18 months)

These are highly useful words that the child uses to express his wants and feelings. Some are names of things and people; some are expressions such as no, yes, good boy; some are words that describe action such as go, up, outside, and eat.

Names One or Two Common Objects from Pictures (18 months)

The child recognizes and can name a few familiar objects in pictures in magazines and books.

Follows Simple Directions (18 to 20 months)

The child can follow verbal directions such as "Bring it to me"; "Put the ball in the box"; "Get your shoes," as long as the directions are about familiar things and are not complicated.

Combines Two or Three Words Spontaneously (20 to 22 months)

The child uses a short phrase such as "go bye-bye," "mommy come," and "go outside." This indicates that he also begins to think in a more connected way and can express his thoughts more completely.

Has Vocabulary of 20 to 50 Words (22 to 24 months)

The size of vocabulary varies. Some children are more fascinated by new words than other children, and are more interested in using them for communication. The size of the vocabulary is also influenced by how much the child is stimulated to speak.

Begins To Use Pronouns I, You, Me (24 months)

The use of the pronouns I, or me, and you is another big event in the speech of the child. It shows that another step has been taken in his awareness of himself as a person separate from others.

Uses Three-Word Sentences (24 months)

Correct grammar is not involved here but there are complete sentences, such as "I (or me) want cookie," and "Mommy not go." At the end of the second year the child has enough words to express his most immediate wishes and his reactions to people and things in his environment. His speech also shows the progress of his ability to think.

Reactions to Others and to Self

Looks at Face of Adult (1 month)

The baby looks directly at the face of another person who comes near, making an eye-to-eye contact.

Smiles Responsively (1½ to 2 months)

This is the social smile, which is seen as the infant's response to social stimulation. When the adult approaches the baby and talk and smiles at him, he gives a responsive smile.

Follows Moving Person Visually (3 months)

The interest of the infant in others, as well as his maturation, is reflected in his ability to continue to look at the adult who moves to and away from him. He can also follow the adult with his eyes as she moves about the room.

Distinguishes "Mother" from Others (3 to 4 months)

This is determined by whether the infant responds differently to the sight of the familiar person and the sound of her voice, than he does to another adult. It usually appears as a more robust and happy response to the familiar person compared to another. This does not mean that he is afraid of others.

Makes Social Contact with People by Smiling or Vocalizing (5 months)

The infant no longer merely responds to social stimulation; he seeks it. He tries to get a response by smiling or vocalizing to a person who is not at that moment attentive to him. It is a natural result of his earlier social contacts.

Plays with Own Foot (5½ to 6 months)

This is part of the behavior that shows the infant's developing awareness of his body. It is most easily observed when he is not being actively stimulated. He reaches and fingers his foot with his hand and may lift his feet to his mouth.

Pushes Away Something He Does Not Want (8 months)

This reflects the infant's ability to push away the adult's hand with his own when the adult tries to do something to him that he does not like, such as when he is approached to have his face washed, nose wiped, or ears cleaned, or when he is offered food or a toy he does not want.

Reacts to Strangers with Anxiety (7 to 8 months)

This reaction is usually seen when an unfamiliar person approaches; the infant's expression becomes serious or he looks distressed. He may cry. The distress may quickly disappear as he becomes accustomed to the new person, and may be hardly noticeable if he is being held by someone he knows well.

Plays Pat-a-cake, So-big, Bye-bye (9 months)

These games are started by the adult and are first seen as social games between the baby and familiar people. The baby will enjoy the play and will imitate it. Later he will start the game himself and expect a response.

Cooperates in Dressing (12 months)

This reflects the infant's participation in the dressing process. He assists by pushing his arm through a sleeve, or his foot into his shoe, for example.

Expresses Many Emotions and Recognizes Them in Others (12 to 14 months)

Many emotions, such as pleasure, anger, anxiety, excitement, and sadness, have been recognized in the baby for some months, but they are especially clear in the beginning of the second year. In addition, he has learned to recognize some of these feelings in others, especially in the familiar adults.

Rolls Ball to Adult with Pleasure (13 to 14 months)

The adult will see this if she rolls a small ball slowly to the infant across the floor or table, and indicates by holding out her hand and by talking to him that she wants him to roll it back. He learns to enjoy this play. Later he will play like this with another child.

Hugs or Gives Kiss to Parent (14 to 15 months)

As one would expect, demonstrating affection develops in the infant only if the adults are affectionate with him and encourage him by saying something like: "Give mommy a hug." At this age, such exchanges are part of the play between adult and child; gradually he learns that it is a way of showing love.

May Show Sharp Separation Reaction (12 to 15 months)

Early in the second year, the toddler may cling or wish to stay close to the adult and may react with distressed crying or become subdued when his "mother" leaves him. Although this can also occur earlier and later, this age period is one during which it may be especially noticeable.

Is Often Negativistic (14 to 16 months)

The growing interest in self-determination may make a child often say "no" at this age, even when he does not mean it.

Identifies Several Parts of Own Body (18 months)

The baby has learned through having this kind of game played with him by the adult to point to his eyes, nose, and other body parts. This is another example of a kind of social interaction that helps the child to learn.

Handles Cup Well (18 to 20 months)

The child can hold a cup firmly and control it well while drinking from it.

Tries To Put On Cap, Mittens, and Other Pieces of Clothing (18 months)

The child has a growing interest in doing more things for himself, including trying to put on some of his clothes.

Feeds Self Well
with Spoon
(21 to 22 months)

At this age, this means spoonfeeding of solid foods with only mimimum spilling. It indicates the child's independent ability to use a feeding utensil properly.

Imitates Adult
Activities
(23 to 24 months)

This is the same as the item in the category on Play and the Use of Toys, but the emphasis here is on the child's imitation of adult activities. This is most easily observed in his imitation of everyday activities at home, such as dusting, sweeping, taking dishes to the sink, putting on some item of the adult's apparel, and driving the car.

Likes To
Please Others
(23 to 24 months)

This varies, of course, but in general the child of 2 has a considerable wish to please adults and to gain their approval.

CHAPTER THIRTEEN

Danger Signals in Development

When an infant is physically ill with an acute infection, we are alerted by such symptoms as fever, listlessness, irritability, vomiting, or a "runny nose." At such times, we expect to find out the reason for his illness and help him to recover. Treatment usually includes specific aid, such medicine, and supporting care, such as feeding him properly and keeping him comfortable.

In regard to an infant's development, also, there are signs and symptoms that alert us when things are not going well. These should be investigated and treated. Most of what is said here applies to infants who are basically normal in their ability to grow and develop but whose development suffers in various ways because of inadequate nurturing (see Chapter 14). Before indicating some of the trouble, however, we will mention other reasons for delayed development.

In any program designed to care for children from early infancy, some infants will be admitted who prove to have inborn defects that prevent normal development. Some of these infants may have an abnormal appearance at birth, but many look quite normal. Brain damage, incomplete development of the brain from various causes, and disorders of metabolism, such as phenylketonuria and thyroid deficiency, are some of the conditions that may occur. Most of these children will have either marked delays in development or physical symptoms that their caretakers will notice early; and the children will then be referred for diagnosis and treatment.

We want to call special attention, however, to these normal infants whose development suffers from insufficient nurturing care, and whose problems may not be so quickly identified. Some of the more frequent difficulties are listed below.

(1) Disturbances in eating or sleeping. Undereating and overeating, as well as undersleeping and oversleeping, may indicate problems. As I have said in the text, the infant's regulation of eating and sleeping are influenced by the quantity and quality of maternal care. There is some evidence that infants in groups tend to sleep and eat excessively when individual attention is difficult or impossible to attain, as when there are many infants and few caretakers. Infants who resist eating and sleeping, especially after they are 3- to 4-months-old tend to be those who have established enough of a relationship to be able to protest or fight. Although this second group is more likely than the first to be developing healthy emotions, long periods of undereating or disturbed sleep suggest that some of a child's important needs are not being met.

(2) Bodily symptoms, such as frequent vomiting, diarrhea, skin rashes, and wheezing may be reactions to problems in nurturing. The mind and body are less separate in infancy than they are later, and there is a strong tendency for the body to express the problems that also involve the emotions. Such symptoms (we call them "psychophysiologic"), have to be distinguished from the vomiting, wheezing, etc. that results from other causes.

(3) Failure to grow normally in height and weight. This may occur, of course, in the infant whose food intake is not adequate. In such cases, we are aware of the child as a poor eater or as one who loses the nourishment through vomiting or diarrhea. But there are other infants who fail to grow in spite of an adequate intake of food. Many of these are infants in whom there appears to be a suppression of those factors within the body that are responsible for normal growth. It has been demonstrated that this can occur to some infants because of an unfavorable emotional climate.

(4) Delay or deviation in specific areas of development. This includes, for example, motor development, communication (verbal and nonverbal) ability, intellectual development, and general learning. It also includes the development of relationships to others, of the sense of self, and the capacity to play. Many aspects of development in these areas have been described, and indeed form a large part of this book. Two questions are useful in assessing these areas of development: (1) What steps has the infant taken in respect to motor development, speech, play, and the other capacities? (2) How does he use these capacities and skills in his adaptation to the opportunities and demands of everyday life? Infants who do not take these developmental steps or who are unable to put their capacities to use are infants in trouble and in need of help.

When a caretaker is concerned about an infant it is important to call upon one's supervisors and upon the social workers, nurses, physicians, and psychologists who are in a position to arrange for a study of the child and make suggestions about how to help him. Sometimes the suggestions will be general ones, following the ideas of the kind of care and environment needed for any child of a given age. At other times, a much more specific prescription of what will help this child at this specific time will be given. People who know in detail about early child development are the consultants needed.

There are two facts of major importance to be borne in mind as we care for infants: One is that their ability to develop can be damaged in situations of poor care, and therefore we must be concerned about what happens to them; the second is that they also have a great drive toward normal development that helps them to resist the damage. This means that we must provide as well as we can, but that our efforts do not have to be perfect in order to get good results.

CHAPTER FOURTEEN

Recommendations to Program Planners

This chapter is a summary of the author's view of the major characteristics of a favorable environment for infants up to the age of 2 years. It implicitly and explicitly emphasizes the importance of the role of the nurturing adult in the development of the infant and indicates some aspects of what is meant by nurture. We hope that it can be used by the agencies, boards, and administrators who plan programs for children living in groups, to emphasize some of the important needs and to stimulate ideas about how such programs can be implemented wherever they are necessary.

The Meaning of It is important that we recognize that the person we select
"Nurture" to care for the babies cannot do so effectively unless those who plan the programs make it possible. Her effectiveness in providing good care will depend upon many things that she does not control, for example, the physical plant and the equipment provided, the number and kind of staff that are budgeted, the policies made by administrators and boards in regard to schedules and routines. It is therefore essential that the community, the boards and administrators, and others in positions of responsibility make it possible for babies to be well cared for by ensuring adequate

financial support and providing competent staff who are aware of and can conduct programs geared to developmental needs of children. The *American College Dictionary* definition of "nurture" is "to feed, nourish, or support during the stages of growth, as children or young; rear. (2) to bring up; train; educate .... nurture suggests tenderness and solicitude in training mind and manners." We can put this in terms of what we as adults must provide—whether we are planners or directly involved in the care of infants in groups. Following are the requirements for providing such nurture:

Attachment to a Specific Person

1. *A person with whom the infant can interact and who responds to his distress signals and to his need for comfort, for relief of tension, and for a social partner.* This is the most important—the need-satisfying adult with whom emotional communication can be established. This is the person who loves and cares for him and whom he loves and trusts. In family life, the mother usually has this role. In situations of group living, however, infants without families need such care from others. If we intend to provide optimal care, the importance of a primary attachment to a specific person cannot be overemphasized. If, because of the realities of scheduling and group living, several caretakers are necessary for each infant, every effort must be made to enable the infant to develop a close attachment to one of them. The provision of care from a variety of people can be adequate, in terms of quantity, to prevent the severe effects of deprivation. It appears, however, that there will be essential differences in the personality development and probably in styles of learning and adaptation between children who develop a strong primary attachment in infancy and those whose attachment is about equally diffused among several "mothers"; and it seems

likely that the differences are entirely detrimental ones for the latter group.

More Staff   This first recommendation—providing sufficient personnel so that a specific primary attachment is possible for every infant—is the most difficult requirement to fulfill and will require major revision of many current practices. It will require a shift in the attitudes of many people who are responsible for planning, financing, or conducting programs for young children in group care. We like to believe that our country values its children highly; yet we lag behind many other countries in financial support and in the quality of care we provide children, especially those who are very young and without families. Improve-
Adequate Pay   ment will require that those who care for children be adequately paid so that more people who are interested in the direct care of children can afford to enter and stay in the field.

In the various group care facilities concerned with daily living, improved care means limiting the number of infants assigned to each "parent"; it means that the straight eight-hour shift, three-shifts-a-day plan will have to be changed, since it cannot possibly provide an infant with the continuity of care he needs. It will mean longer time spans during the day when the infant's principal care-taker is available to him—at least a 12-hour period so that
Continuity of Care   his getting-up and going-to-bed times are covered. Hours off during the day could be arranged for the caretaker by use of a regular substitute. Some of the people who participate in the care of the children during the day and whom the children learn to know must be available to them at night. This will require that some caretakers live in; others may sleep in when necessary. When the child is ill, it will be necessary that his principal caretaker be in

more constant attendance; planning for this will require adequate compensation in money and later time off.

Infants should be cared for by people who want to care for them, who have something to give, and who can get satisfaction from what the infant gives to them in return. But those who plan and supervise the programs must see to it that these crucially important persons are valued and adequately supported so that, insofar as is humanly possible in group care, those conditions that help the child to develop in a healthy way are created. Without a serious commitment to providing continuity of caretakers and minimizing changes we cannot possibly provide good care.

Care and Supplies 2. *Adequate food, clothing, and shelter to support growth and health, prevent physical illness through various protective measures; and personnel to attend promptly when illnesses occur.* This is the easiest of the conditions to fulfill and in most group settings in recent years has been conscientiously provided and maintained. Conditions that protect the physical health of the infant have been spelled out clearly in health codes of public health agencies, and in recommendations of physicians and other health personnel on the prevention and treatment of illness.

Physical Handling 3. *Physical handling in the holding, cuddling, bathing, lifting, changing of clothing, and other everyday events that are a part of infant care.* These experiences are rich in social communications besides being necessary for nourishment and comfort. They are important in the development of gross motor skills, for development of the child's concept of his body self, and for development of the capacity to act. Intentional action (action that the infant takes to gain an end) in relation to the external environment is an essential step in his development. It influences what he learns about his physical and social environment through active observation, manipulation, play, exploration, and experimentation. Intentional action also helps him to experience and understand his own abilities and limitations, for example, when he can cope with a situation or master a skill through his own activity, and when he needs help. Much of this action is, of course, interaction with others, especially with the parent figures who respond to and stimulate his actions. They help him in the long and ever-changing process of learning by encouraging some of his actions and by limiting others.

A Speaking Social Partner

4. *A speaking social partner. It is unlikely that language can develop adequately if the infant is not spoken to.* The speech of the adult is one of the principal channels through which information comes to the infant about himself and his world, who and what he is, how he feels, what he is doing, and so on. It labels and provides information about the people, things, and experiences in his life. His first meaningless babblings can be reinforced and interpreted in such a way that his repertoire of sounds with specific meaning steadily increases, and he learns to speak. Talking to a child, it is believed, also provides extremely important influences in the development of his thinking. This is especially apparent in the second year when the early phases of the development of logical thought, symbolic thought, and inner mental representations of people and things become evident in the child's own speech and behavior.

Consistency and Repetition

5. *An atmosphere in which consistency and repetition are prominent.* Such an atmosphere helps to create in the infant a physical and mental state that supports learning and adaptation. Consistency and repetition provide significant periods of time when the infant is free of major discomfort and excessive tension and therefore able to give attention. This situation is made possible mainly by

the consistency and presence of the person who cares for him in a certain way day after day. It is a natural part of a good family environment. In group care, however, this becomes a problem, because even with a favorable arrangement the child will have to relate to more different caretakers than is ideal, and continuity is hard to achieve. Too often, routinizing and rigid scheduling are substituted in group care for the continuity of the caretaking person. It is extremely important to realize that the consistency of which we speak resides mainly in the people and not in the clock, and that excessive routinization and rigidity must be guarded against.

Variety and Contrast

6. *Variety and contrast within the atmosphere created by consistency and repetition.* It is believed that variety and contrast sharpen the infant's perceptions and awareness and create those mild tension states that call for an adaptive response from the child. As long as the tension state is not so massive as to overwhelm and disorganize, it serves as a stimulus to development. Group settings have tended to be deficient in providing variety and contrast. A monotonous, bland environment fails to meet the child's needs, because it does not stimulate him to look, to act, to listen, or in other ways to use or develop his faculties.

Playthings

7. *Toys and other playthings.* While a responsive human partner is crucial to his development, the infant has need also for experiences with toys and other materials that he can use independently. Toys bring to the infant a variety of stimuli, challenges, and satisfactions because of their structure, color, texture, form, and other physical qualities that support intellectual development. They are also important as objects that infants can use to discharge feelings of aggression, pleasure, and excitement without getting back a response. As he grows older, he uses them to support his imaginative play, and they are used by him in

working out some of the problems that occur in the long process of developing controls and becoming responsible for his own behavior.

Opportunities To Move About

8. *Opportunities to move about, to play, and to use the emerging skills and dispositions in a supportive and safe atmosphere.* A combination of freedom and protection becomes increasingly important to the child toward the end of the first year as he becomes a toddler. In addition to enlarging his experience and stimulating mental and physical development, moving about and playing contribute to the development of the awareness of his own body and person—the development of the sense of self as distinct from all others, and of what he himself can do. These opportunities should not be difficult to provide if enough adults are around. This emphasizes the importance in group care settings of having enough adults or responsible older children to keep an eye on the young children.

Moments of Peace

9. *Moments of peace during which the infant is not asked to interact with people or other outside stimuli.* This may sound strange, since infants have more often been alone too much in group care settings, but an infant does need peaceful, quiet moments. They help to replenish his energies and allow him time to begin to be aware that he has an inner world of thought, fantasy, and feeling. A constantly stimulating, highly charged environment is not conducive to a harmonious balance between the child's outer and inner worlds. In planning the group care setting, it is important to provide enough space to allow for areas or rooms in which quietness and privacy are possible.

Appropriate Limits

10. *Limits, prohibitions, and frustrations appropriate to the age of the child.* This recommendation should not be interpreted as favoring a punitive, animal-trainer approach to the child. Rather, what is referred to here is the adult's role in helping the child to learn how to wait for some-

thing, how to behave toward others, how to recognize danger, and to learn what he is permitted and what he is not permitted to do. Putting requirements upon him that are appropriate to his stage of development helps the infant learn to live with others in a society that has particular customs, ideals, and standards.

Such social requirements—demands upon the child—inevitably give rise to anxiety, frustration, displeasure, and conflict within the child. It is important for adults to realize that aggressive angry feelings, which are often expressed by hitting, crying, biting, and so on, are normal and healthy and should be expected. Adults can help the child to learn a way of expressing these feelings that will neither harm others nor get him into trouble or danger. He should be allowed to protest and complain, though he is not given license to abuse others physically; there should be a few things in his vicinity that he can bang, throw, or treat roughly in his anger. Then he can be calmed or comforted, if he needs to be, because a child who has just had an angry outburst is often in need of reassurance that he has not alienated the adult by his behavior. Although states of tension and discomfort are essential to a child's development and learning, it seems safe to say that in infancy, at least, the best development takes place in a setting in which comfort and pleasure predominate over discomfort and frustration.

For the most part, the education and guidance of the infant, which are essential to his development, should take place in an atmosphere of loving attention. Such an atmosphere in a group care setting is dependent upon having enough people with enough time interested in particular infants.

Introducing Men   11. *An opportunity to know men.* The world of children in group care settings tends to be a world of women. In the earliest months of life this is no special disadvantage for the infant, since direct involvement in infant care is not a major role of fathers and father substitutes. As the infant becomes a toddler, however, it becomes increasingly important that he have an opportunity to know men. The situation in group care, of course, will be different from the usual family and will have to be planned. Various people can satisfy this need: (1) Husbands of the women caring for the children who live with their wives in the group care setting but work outside. If such men are willing to be even superficially involved with the infants, when they come home evenings, it can be helpful. (2) Men who work in or around the group care residence. They may be administrators, maintenance staff, social workers or psychologists, part time physicians, or the occasional repair man or delivery man. Though not caretakers of the children, these men can be encouraged to talk with the children and to permit the children to observe and be interested in what they are doing. (3) Older boys or men who can assist in the care of the infants, particularly by directing outings or supervising play activities. Also, they may be present, perhaps, at mealtime.

As such efforts are made, other possibilities will develop. The important thing for program planners is that children need to have men in their environment from infancy onward, and that program planners must include this.

The Adult World   12. *Opportunities for the child to be a part of the adult world.* The importance to the child of being a participant in the world of the adult was emphasized recently by Dr. Sibylle Escalona in a workshop on group residential care of young children and was discussed by Anna Freud and other members of the workshop.[1] Escalona commented that in most child care programs, staff members—whether cook, laundress, or the person directly responsible for the child—are geared to providing care for the children. She pointed out that, in a family setting, the mother has to respond to many other demands not related directly to infant care, such as preparing dinner for the family, attending to household chores, entertaining friends or relatives, and taking older children to school. These events, responsibilities, or pressures become a part of the child's experience with his mother. This is one of the ways in which he builds up his view of what we call reality. Freud, in emphasizing Escalona's point, said that the child in a family is involved in the world of the adults and participates in it while being cared for by them. This participation enriches his experience in countless ways and includes the important communication that he and his family are parts of a larger society.

Caretakers'
Other Duties
How might such experience be achieved in group care? Those who care for the children should have other duties—cleaning, cooking, marketing, washing—that the child can become aware of as going on about him and that cannot always be set aside immediately for him. There is another important facet to this type of experience, which has to do with the child's gradually learning that some things happen which the adults who care for him cannot control, that his "mother" may be as disappointed as he is that an outing is canceled, or that she has pleasures and disappointments that have nothing to do with him. One way of trying to provide such richness of experiences is to

1. Workshop on Group Residential Care of Infants and Young Children, April 1966, sponsored by the Research Division of the U.S. Children's Bureau and the Yale Child Study Center. The proceedings are being published by the Children's Bureau under the title *Rearing Infants and Young Children in Institutions.*

make it possible for friends of the child care workers to visit for meals or at other times; to encourage the caretakers to take the child along on some of their outside activities; to make mealtimes a social time for the adults too, so that they have an opportunity to talk together about whatever they wish. Another helpful procedure is to build into the program some possibilities for the "parent" to have things to do while she is in the child care center that are for herself as a person and are independent of her role as caretaker of children and that the child can know about—that is, he is "around" while she is doing them.

In other words, it seems reasonable to propose that although care of the child is the prime function of the setting, the setting should not be exclusively child-centered. Such an atmosphere cannot be accomplished in a setting in which duties are sharply divided and there is an eight-hour, three-shift arrangement of caretakers. If we are willing to break with some traditional patterns of child-caring institutions and devise new ways in which we can permit the child to have some part in the adult world, many more ways of encouraging this will occur to us.

CHAPTER FIFTEEN

A Personal Note to Those
Who Take Care of Infants

Your
Contribution

This book, as we have said, is for people taking care of infants not their own. You, for whom it is written, have undertaken a valuable work. There is nothing more important than our children. We all earnestly hope that the next generations will be able to work for and live in peace and brotherhood. There may seem to be a great distance between the dependent infant and the diplomat, atomic scientist, devoted parent, or responsible citizen, but we believe that there can be no more important contribution to the future than helping children get off to a good start in life. Some of you who have chosen this work may be fully aware of the contribution you make; others of you may be more influenced by the immediate enjoyment that caring for babies gives. Whatever your reasons, there are times when you will feel great satisfaction, other times when you will be bored, dissatisfied, and ready to give up.

You do not work alone in your care of infants. There are social workers, pediatricians and other physicians, psychologists, nurses, and many others whose professional work is concerned mainly with child health and welfare. There are private and government agencies and organizations whose major responsibility is in the same area. In your local situation, there are undoubtedly supervisors, consultants, and administrators to whom you can turn when you are worried about a specific infant or about your concerns and frustrations in the work.

Interest and Patience

While many of you derive great satisfaction from child care, it is not always easy to give of yourself generously and lovingly to an infant—especially to one who is not your own. Neither is it easy to summon the interest and patience to care for several infants at the same time. Many of the everyday details of infant care are difficult: the incessant diaper changes, the mopping up of spilled milk, having to leave something in which you are involved to respond to a crying child, the almost constant need to look ahead to what comes next, the necessity to put aside your own fatigue to take care of a sick or distressed infant. The number and kind of tasks involved can be only a burden and a bore unless you are able to enjoy much of what goes on between yourself and the child and to take pleasure in watching him grow and change from day to day.

Spontaneity

The suggestions and information given in this guide are not intended to make you self-conscious or afraid to be natural and spontaneous. There is a danger in trying to plan every word or action because such self-consciousness may make people afraid to express their feelings, and they then behave in a constricted and artificial way that is not good for them and limits the child's experience. Being able to accept that you will have negative feelings, too, and that you will be impatient as well as patient, irritable as well as accepting, and childish as well as mature in your behavior is an important part of your view of yourself as a person caring for children.

The suggestions in this book are given in the hope that they will help you to understand the importance to the infant of being cared for by people who can give of themselves. They should increase your self-esteem. And, when we know that our work has meaning, we all have more energy and can give a little more.

Enjoyment We hope that you can enjoy your work at least most of the time, even though it has its unpleasant aspects. Infant care should not be grim and unpleasant; laughter and fun are important. For those who take the time to enjoy it, there is no greater pleasure and gratification than that given by the child to the person who cares for him. We hope that you are adeqately paid in money also, because none of us can expect ourselves to work only for the intangible satisfactions in the job, no matter how great they are.

These days in the young child's life are important to him in the many ways mentioned in this book and more. But they are the days of your life, too, and they should be days lived with pleasure and with realization of your own worth.

Suggested Readings

Bowlby, John, *Child Care and the Growth of Love,* abridged from *Maternal Care and Mental Health.* Baltimore, Penguin Books, 1953.

Fraiberg, Selma H., *The Magic Years.* New York, Charles Scribner's Sons, 1959. A rich source of information about early child development and some of the problems of early childhood.

Infant Care. Washington, D.C., U.S. Government Printing Office, 1963. A helpful source of information about infant care and general development.

Murphy, Lois Barclay, and Associates, *The Widening World of Childhood.* New York, Basic Books, 1962.

Provence, Sally, M.D., and Lipton, Rose C., *Infants in Institutions—A Comparison of Their Development with Family-Reared Infants During the First Year of Life.* New York, International Universities Press, 1962. A report of a research study comparing a group of infants living in an institution with a group of those living in families.

Ribble, Margaret A., *The Rights of Infants,* 2nd ed. New York, Columbia University Press, 1965.

Thomas, Alexander, *et al., Behavioral Individuality in Early Childhood.* New York, New York University Press, 1963.

Yarrow, Leon J. "Separation from Parents During Early Childhood," in Martin L. and Lois Wladis Hoffman, eds., *Re-*

view of Child Development Research, Vol. I. New York, Russell Sage Foundation, 1964. A review article that summarizes many of the studies on separation and discusses the implications.

Your Child from One to Six. Washington, D.C., U.S. Government Printing Office, 1962. Recommended for informa-

Your Child from One to Six. Washington, D.C., U.S. Govern-